Report Writing for Crime Scene Investigators

Report Writing for Crime Scene Investigators provides students with the tools to write effective crime scene reports. Students looking to break into the field of crime scene investigations often take courses in report writing but the textbooks available are commonly geared toward general law enforcement and first responders. However, none of the books on the market focus on the craft of effective, informative writing with graphic crime scene-specific considerations in mind. While falling under law enforcement's purview, crime scene investigations fall within the forensic science field, and, as such, the reporting required is more technical and often more scientific in nature than the average police report.

Due to the lack of published resources and guidance in this critical area, there is no standard that currently exists for vital function within the crime scene and investigative circles – and often the subject is given short shrift. This creates wide discrepancies among what students are being taught. This book is the first of its kind to provide students, and those professionals and agencies in need of a "blueprint", with a resource to teach them various types of reports – and how to refer to scenarios and specific types of evidence – to ensure that the report holds up under the process of an investigation and for use within the courts.

Key features:

- Outlines the key distinctions between police-style reports and crime scene-style reports and writing
- Explains how to clearly and accurately provide an accounting and description of a variety of evidence recovered from a scene
- Details how to best organize the report in a logical manner and sequence, including the various components of the crime scene report

- Presents an explanation of the information that should be included in the report, and the rationale behind its importance, for testimonial purposes

Report Writing for Crime Scene Investigators provides to the reader the fundamentals of effective report writing for the active field crime scene investigations. Coverage includes the necessary steps to thoroughly document scenes and evidence – from the time the CSI receives the call until the time the CSI testifies in court. In addition to the student market, this book will be a welcome resource for professional crime scene investigators and attorneys and a reference and standard for professional training programs.

Report Writing for Crime Scene Investigators

Laura Pazarena, Michael Kessler,
and Amy Watroba

CRC Press is an imprint of the
Taylor & Francis Group, an **informa** business

First edition published 2022
by CRC Press
6000 Broken Sound Parkway NW, Suite 300, Boca Raton, FL 33487-2742

and by CRC Press
4 Park Square, Milton Park, Abingdon, Oxon, OX14 4RN

CRC Press is an imprint of Taylor & Francis Group, LLC

ISBN: 9780367359959 (hbk)
ISBN: 9780367359973 (pbk)
ISBN: 9780429343162 (ebk)

DOI: 10.4324/9780429343162

Typeset in Caslon
by Deanta Global Publishing Services, Chennai, India

Dedicated to my mother, Laura Pazarena, who did not
live long enough to see this dream become a reality,
and to my father, Alexander Pazarena, who did.

Contents

List of Figures

Acknowledgments

This text has been a longtime goal and would not have come to fruition if it had not been for the support of our friends, family, co-workers, and all those we have learned from in our careers. We cannot thank all the professionals in our lives enough for taking the time to teach and mold us into the investigators we are today. Every agency and person that we have ever met has had an influence on who we are, and we thank them all dearly!

First, I would like to thank and acknowledge my parents (Alex and Laura) and my siblings (Matt, Alex, James, and Christine), thank you for supporting and encouraging me through all these years.

Shannon and Lainie, I appreciate you, your optimism, and positivity.

Wiggins, you'll always be my partner and wifey, thank you!

Leonie (and Gummy), I would not be where I am without your lifelong friendship!

Vern and Tammi, bet it all!

Ephryn Thompson, you have balanced me and truly supported me in every endeavor. I am so grateful to have you in my life as a partner, cheerleader, and sounding board. Thank you for everything you do for me every day, you're appreciated more than you will ever know!

Lastly, to every agency, military branch, and investigative division I've ever had the pleasure of working with, thank you for all that you do. Your dedication to this field is motivating to me every day and pushes me to be better, thank you for all you have done for me, and all you do for others in your daily profession.

About the Authors

Laura Pazarena, MFS, CSCSA, is a medicolegal death investigator with the State of North Carolina's Chief Medical Examiner's Office and an adjunct professor of criminal justice and crime scene investigations at Broward College. She began her career as a police officer and quickly advanced into the Crime Scene Unit where her sole function was processing various crime scenes forensically. She deployed to Afghanistan to assist with the establishment of forensic labs for the Department of Defense. During her two-year deployment she was a part of the set-up of several labs that involved the forensic exploitation of improvised explosive devices, and she managed the oversight and chain of custody of thousands of items of evidence. She was the supervisor of the Evidence Unit and worked in the fingerprint and chemistry sections doing a forensic analysis of evidence recovered by military personnel. Upon her return, she continued as a forensic subject matter expert for the Department of Defense. She then went to Florida where she created the Forensic Unit for the Flagler County Sheriff's Office. Using her expertise in crime scene investigations she created the agency's general orders, standard operating procedures, reports, templates, documents, and training manuals for crime scene investigation and response and assisted in agency accreditation. She managed the Evidence Unit and assisted in proper personnel training and created the agency's Evidence Submission Manual. Her continued desire to educate and train led her to become an adjunct professor and then a full-time assistant professor of crime scene investigations. She continues to teach and train students and new investigators in both of her current jobs.

She is a member of numerous forensic organizations including the International Association of Identification (IAI), the Florida Division of the International Association of Identification (FDIAI), and the American Association of Forensic Science (AAFS). She is a certified senior crime scene analyst through the IAI, she holds a bachelor of science degree in chemistry and forensic science and a master's degree in forensic science, and has a published articles in the *Journal of Forensic Science and Criminology*.

Michael P. Kessler, PSM-FS, IAI-CCSA, MCSFS, Forensics & Public Safety Manager, Denton Police Department (Texas), is an internationally recognized Forensic/Crime Scene Investigation subject matter expert with nearly twenty years of experience. He holds a Professional Science Master's Degree in Forensic Science from Florida International University (FIU). He is a leader in standards development in crime scene investigation including with NIST's OSAC and AAFS's ASB. Michael's experience includes high-profile, counterterrorism investigations, crimes against persons, financial crimes, and volume/property crimes. Michael has worked investigations in collaboration with numerous prestigious investigative and intelligence agencies globally including the Texas Rangers, FBI, ATF, DEA, NCIS, USACID, AFOSI, RCMP, MetPol SO15, DIA, CIA, and USSOCOM.

Amy Watroba is a career trial and appellate prosecutor who concentrates on litigating cases involving complex DNA and forensic science issues, providing legal support and training for attorneys, law enforcement officers, and scientists, and developing policies and procedures related to forensic evidence.

Ms. Watroba has prosecuted high-profile and serious felony jury and bench trials involving complex DNA (RFLP, PCR/STR, Y-STR, mtDNA, parentage), serology, microscopy, trace chemistry, firearms identification, bloodstain pattern analysis, forensic pathology, historic cell tower analysis, and fingerprint evidence. She has litigated appeals in the Supreme Court of the United States, Illinois Supreme Court, and Illinois Appellate Court.

Ms. Watroba is a member of the National District Attorneys Association's DNA Advisory Committee, four of the American Academy of Forensic Sciences' Consensus Bodies, and the FBI's Rapid DNA Task Force and was appointed by the Illinois governor to serve on the Governor's Task Force on Forensic Science. She instructs prosecutors from across the country for the NDAA, presents training programs for law enforcement agencies and forensic testing laboratories, and has served as a volunteer trial team coach and guest instructor for law school courses at several Chicago law schools. Ms. Watroba received the NDAA's 2021 Distinguished Faculty Award.

Ms. Watroba received her law degree from Loyola University – Chicago School of Law in 2001. She graduated with Honors from the University of Michigan – Ann Arbor in 1998 with a B.A. in creative writing.

SECTION 1

Fundamentals of Report Writing

1

INTRODUCTION

LAURA PAZARENA

Introduction

Crime scene investigators (CSIs) are responsible for the forensic processing of crime scenes and evidence. After completing their processing, the CSI must explain in detail all the work they did in reports and/or sketches. The CSI's employer will have policies, procedures, and guidelines for report writing, and this text will serve as a good guide for CSIs when writing various types of reports. CSIs most frequently work with law enforcement or other criminal justice professionals, and their only report writing guide is from these individuals. CSI reports, however, are unique reports and should be written differently from other reports in this field.

Police Reports

Criminal justice personnel respond to a variety of offenses and incidents. Many of the cases that police officers are involved in are incidents that will never go to court; however, reports of their response and investigative findings must still be written. Report writing is a basic fundamental that police officers often dread but must learn how to do well. A ***police report*** is a report written by a police officer about an incident or case and is considered a statement made by the police officer who wrote it. A police report may be used to make charging decisions in criminal cases, during depositions, and in court as part of civil litigation and criminal prosecutions. It also may be viewed by members of the media and the public. Officers want to ensure they are writing clear and understandable reports. Other people will judge an officer's work and professionalism based on a report before meeting them in person, which is why having good writing skills is very

DOI: 10.4324/9780429343162-2

important in the criminal justice field. Police reports are one of the most crucial components of a criminal investigation. When officers write reports, they are interested in obtaining the circumstances surrounding an event to determine if there is probable cause for an arrest or to help them decide if the situation is an incident with no crime. Generally, they obtain this information from ***testimonial evidence***, which consists of people's statements to them. Officers will interview individuals on the scene, canvass for witnesses, and look for people to tell them about what may have happened. Their reports will include the details of who they spoke to, when they spoke to them, and what was said. Their focus is generally on the people of the case. Police reports also should mention any physical evidence that they observe on a scene. Officers are usually one of the first groups of individuals to arrive at a major scene, and they observe the scene as close to its original condition as anyone. It is imperative that they take photos, use body-worn cameras, or take notes of what they see when they arrive. Although they generally focus on the people, the context of the evidence within a scene at the time of their arrival may be critical to the crime scene investigator (CSI). Police reports do not generally convey the condition of the scene or the physical evidence, which is why a specific CSI report is so important (see Figure 1.1).

CSI Reports

Forensic science is a vast field that encompasses numerous disciplines. One of the most overlooked components of this ever-growing field is crime scene investigation. In the criminal justice world, crime scene investigators (CSIs) are often referred to as "trash collectors", and their scientific expertise and crime scene reconstruction skills are often undermined or ignored. CSIs offer valuable insight into a criminal investigation. Their expertise is crucial in regard to evidence collection and processing and especially scene reconstruction. Unfortunately, many CSIs are never taught how to properly document and report their crucial findings. CSIs often are shown repeatedly how to properly photograph but rarely do they take specific courses on report writing. Usually, the report writing they are shown is inaccurate and inadequate for the technical field of crime scene investigation. If CSIs are fortunate enough to take a report writing course,

On Monday, January 8, 2018, at approximately 0940 hours, Officer Pazarena was working full duty, in full uniform, driving a marked police vehicle, when she received a radio dispatch in regards to a weapons complaint. Dispatch advised Officer Pazarena to respond to 1234 Main Street. There were no reported injuries on scene. Upon arrival on scene Officer Pazarena met the complainant Mr. Doe.

Mr. Doe was interviewed and he stated the following:

Unknown subject(s) shot at his residence, 1234 Main Street, sometime during the previous night. Mr. Doe did not know the exact time the shooting may have taken place. He reported that he left his home at 2100 hours and when he returned home at 0930 hours he observed light coming into the garage. He opened the garage door and found a mark on the left hand side of the interior of the garage.

Mr. Doe showed Officer Pazarena the damage to the side of his residence as well as the location of several cartridge casings. The cartridge casings were found at the northeast corner of Main Street and Live Street. Officer Pazarena found four cartridge casings in this vicinity and marked them with traffic cones for the Crime Scene Investigator.

Officer Pazarena observed the damage to the garage door and the home that Mr. Doe pointed out. There was one hole in the garage door. There were three marks along the east exterior wall of the residence. While observing the damage to the home Officer Pazarena observed three holes to a fence belonging to the neighbor directly east of Mr. Doe's home. The address of this home was 1235 Main Street.

Officer Pazarena responded to 1235 Main Street to contact a homeowner. Mrs. Smith answered the door. Mrs. Smith was interviewed and she stated the following:

Mrs. Smith stated that her husband had put a trailer into their yard through the gate a week ago and there were no holes in the fence at that time. Mrs. Smith stated that she went to bed around midnight the previous night and did not hear any sounds that could have been gunshots during the night. She further reported that her dogs normally bark at loud sounds and would have more than likely reacted to sounds of gunshots and they did not make any sounds during the night.

Officer Pazarena asked both Mr. Doe and Mrs. Smith if they had home surveillance cameras. Neither homeowner did.

Officer Pazarena then conducted a neighborhood canvas. The following addresses were attemtped with negative results:

1244 Main Street, 1236 Main Street, 1242 Main Street

When Crime Scene Investigator (CSI) West arrived on scene Officer Pazarena conducted a walk-through of the scene. CSI West was shown the locations of all damage and the cartridge casings.

After CSI West completed processing the scene the scene was cleared.

No further action taken by Officer Pazarena.

Figure 1.1 Example narrative of a police report. Notice all the testimonial evidence within this narrative.

they are often taught how to write reports in a police writing format, which couldn't be further from how a CSI should be writing. CSI reports are written by CSIs and are technical reports that are very different from law enforcement reports. CSI reports should explain processing mechanisms and results utilizing proper terminology. A CSI must understand the scientific concepts and be able to explain these mechanisms in layman's terms to a court and jury.

CSI reports are a critical part of scene documentation that contemporaneously and comprehensively record – from start to finish – the procedures, observations, actions, and aspects of the scene and evidence within it. Scene documentation has a three-fold significance: investigative, scientific, and legal, requiring that reporting be thorough and accurate.

Scene documentation is conducted to create a fair, factual, and accurate record of the observations, conditions, and actions at a given scene and its immediate surroundings. Documentation provides the basis from which a scene reconstruction could be created from the documentation alone. Documentation also supports all scene-processing work such that another examiner or analyst could evaluate what was done and understand the basis of the results.

The Scientific Method

Crime scene investigators must remember that the processing of a scene is a science. They should always apply the basic principles of the scientific method to their processing and report writing. The scientific method begins with a *question*. In most cases for a CSI, the question is, "What happened here?" – or something to that effect. The CSI will discuss the case with the investigators during the initial brief, gather background information, and observe the scene and evidence to develop a *hypothesis*, the second phase of the scientific method. An important note about this phase is that detectives and officers will begin to build their hypotheses of the events based on the testimonial evidence. The CSI must remember not to allow testimonial evidence or the officers' hypotheses to steer their observations of the physical evidence on the scene and what that evidence might be saying. The CSI will utilize the physical evidence on the scene to develop their own hypothesis, which may or may not contradict or support the testimonial evidence.

Once a CSI has a hypothesis in mind, they must develop a thought experiment in the context of the available information and physical evidence. While a crime scene reconstruction often involves physical experiments to test hypotheses under controlled conditions, a ***thought experiment*** is a device with which one performs an intentional, structured process of intellectual deliberation in order to speculate, within the confines of the scene and physical evidence, about the potential occurrence of events and the sequencing of events. For a CSI, this means putting together the "what ifs" on the scene. Looking at the physical evidence, possible answers to questions will begin to develop. The evidence does not lie. The CSI must start to think of alternative ways for the items to have landed in their positions. This is the experimentation phase of the scientific method. The CSI will experiment with all possible options, not just the one that confirms an original hypothesis.

The CSI must continue to play out various scenarios and alternate hypotheses and discuss these options with the detective or in their notes and thoughts. This *data collection* will begin to eliminate specific options. The CSI will *analyze* each of these possibilities and exclude the impossible. The evidence will lead the CSI to a plausible solution to the hypothesis. All of the evidence and steps involved in the investigation must then be *reported* (Figure 1.2).

The CSI will report the facts from the scene as observed. This report must be detailed, accurate, and understandable and should include all pertinent facts and conditions of the scene. The CSI must ensure never to infer anything or give their opinion. The CSI should report what items are actually on the scene and what they see, not what others told them should be there or what someone else saw. CSIs must remain neutral and report everything as they observe it. The report should flow chronologically and include all involvement of the CSI

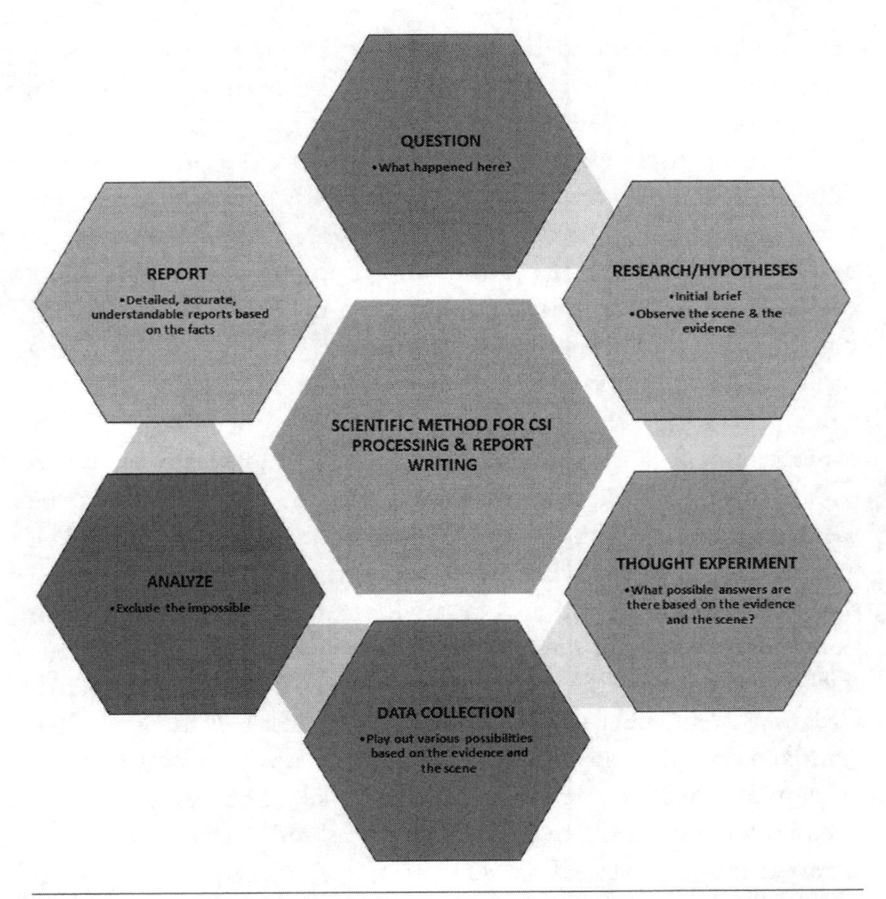

Figure 1.2 The scientific method for CSI processing and report writing.

from the time they received the call until the conclusion of the scene processing. For complicated scenes, the flow of the report is crucial to help law enforcement officers, attorneys, the court, a jury, and the CSI understand the order of events and processing. Timing is critical in a criminal investigation, and when and why a CSI did specific processing may significantly impact a case.

Crime scene investigators should always attempt any processing techniques that may obtain results, no matter the likelihood. Often these attempts are futile and will result in negative results. These processing attempts should always be included in the CSI's notes and reports. These negative results often lead a CSI to try other methods or techniques and explain why a CSI moved onto other items or locations for processing. CSIs must remember to report the processing that yielded positive results and the processing that yielded negative results. CSIs should understand the science behind every processing method they employ and be prepared to explain in court why a certain process may not have worked.

The scene itself may dictate what kinds of processing may be done, so it is imperative that crime scene investigators describe the scene in detail in words in their report. CSIs must remember to explain places as if the people they are talking to have no idea where the CSI was because this is the situation in many cases. The CSI must describe the general area the scene was located. Are you in a residential neighborhood or at the beach? These two locations make scene processing very different and unique and need to be clearly explained. Full factual descriptions of the scenes, both inside and outside if applicable, should be included. The descriptions of the scenes should match the photographs of the scenes that were taken and explain in writing what is depicted in the pictures. A part of the scene description should also be any damage to the location, such as broken windows or door frames. These types of scene conditions may help the CSI with their hypothesis of the events that occurred. CSIs must remember to state the facts only; just because a window is broken does not mean that someone broke in. It is a fact that the window is broken, how the window got broken, and how long it has been broken for is unknown and therefore should not be inferred or reported by the CSI. All of the facts of the evidence found on the scene will lead readers – such as police officers, prosecutors, defense attorneys, and other CSIs – to infer their own conclusions. CSIs should never infer for the reader.

Crime scene investigators are always concerned with weather conditions. This information is not only useful when it comes to how to dress and prepare for the scene personally but may also indicate why a CSI may do one process versus another or none at all. The weather conditions are essential at the time of the scene processing. CSIs are often called hours before a search warrant is obtained or hours after an event has occurred. The weather conditions at the time of the call should be indicated in the Overview section of the report if the weather prior to the CSI's arrival may have an impact on the scene. If, for example, the CSI is told it was storming prior to their arrival, this may indicate why the CSI is observing some anomalies on the scene, such as the decedent being wet. The weather conditions at the time of the processing may impact what a CSI can do on the scene and should be clearly reported.

The crime scene investigator (CSI) documents scenes in a variety of ways. Four main components of crime scene documentation include note-taking, photography, reports, and sketching. Some CSIs will also do videography of their scenes which adds a fifth documentation element to some scenes. The report is where the CSI will indicate all documentation that was done on a crime scene. The CSI must be specific as to who did each phase of documentation and what was done. The end goal of any criminal investigation is prosecution in a court of law. Attorneys must be able to clearly understand who completed all phases of the processing so all personnel may be called to testify if needed. The CSI must also indicate where this crucial documentation may be found. Attorneys will need to have copies of all sources of documentation and will need to know if they are looking for compact discs, hard drives, or digital copies of images, videos, etc.

One of the most important parts of crime scene investigation is the proper collection and documentation of evidence. A criminal case may be won or lost based on the handling of the evidence. What items were collected, who collected them, and how they were collected are critical components in any criminal case. A CSI wants to ensure that this information is easily accessible and understandable in the report. Trivial parts of the report, such as paragraphs and tabbing, become critical to the CSI that is testifying to a 15-page report and trying to find every cartridge casing listed in the report. The evidence listed in the report should always match the photographs of the evidence that was taken on the scene and in the lab. The CSI may easily be discredited on the stand with any discrepancies in their reporting or documentation related to a case.

Police Reports versus CSI Reports

Similar to police officers, CSIs often do not enjoy report writing. It is no accident that television and movie depictions of CSIs do not include report writing – reports may become tedious, repetitive, and lengthy. The CSI must understand, however, that their report will be viewed by many people even if they themselves never attend court. Their report must explain the work they did in a clear and concise manner, so anyone who reads it can understand the events and has a professional interpretation of the CSI who wrote it.

As previously mentioned, CSI reports are technical, scientific reports that explain the facts about the relationship between the crime scene, the physical evidence, and any processing that was done. In stark contrast to a police report, CSI reports generally do not include testimonial evidence or what people said. CSIs deal with the physical evidence and their reports should detail and document what the evidence is, where it was found, and the condition it was in. CSIs do not regularly talk to witnesses or other people, so their reports do not often include information about the people involved in a case. Police reports, however, are quite frequently full of details about what other people saw and did.

Importance of CSI Reports

Although CSIs in some jurisdictions are sworn officers, their reports are not the same as police reports. CSIs serve a different function within the criminal justice system. They are there to assist with the documentation and interpretation of physical evidence on a scene. They perform detailed processing of evidence and crime scenes using a variety of chemicals and processes, and they complete photography and detailed sketches of scenes. Their reports must detail all of the technical work they do, the physical evidence they observed, and what was done with that evidence. In most courts, CSIs are the criminal justice personnel who are able to testify to photographs and evidence in order to enter them into evidence for consideration by a judge or jury. CSI reports are crucial to assist the CSI in preparing to testify about what they observed and did on scene and to explain the photos and evidence related to their work that is admitted into evidence in court. CSI reports also explain the technical processes that were done on scene and in the lab. CSI reports are critical to how important evidence ultimately is presented in court.

Summary

CSI reports are intrinsically different from police reports. Although both the CSI and the investigating officers are writing about the same case, the focus of each report is very different. CSIs are more concerned with physical evidence and using that evidence to support or refute the testimonial evidence the investigating officers collect. Learning how to write a CSI report using the correct terminology and scientific knowledge of the field is imperative for CSIs when testifying in court and explaining their expertise on the scene. CSIs will not testify in court for every case they work on, but their reports will be seen by many and should be written in a manner that shows the CSI's professionalism, experience, and knowledge in their field.

End of Chapter Questions

1. What is the difference between a CSI report and a police report?
2. Why is it important to have a specific CSI report?
3. What is testimonial evidence?
4. What is the three-fold significance of scene documentation?
5. What is a thought experiment?
6. How does a CSI use the scientific method in report writing?

2

Writing Succinctly Utilizing Proper Spelling, Grammar, and Terminology

LAURA PAZARENA

Succinct Writing

The Merriam-Webster Dictionary defines *succinct* as: "marked by compact precise expression without wasted words". Being succinct in report writing is important to quickly get the reader to understand what the crime scene investigator (CSI) is trying to express. Superfluous wording can make reports confusing and convoluted. A CSI must clearly explain what a scene looked like, what they did on the scene, and what processes were done – but this must be described factually and briefly. Describing a scene is very important for the reader. A CSI must clearly depict what they saw. The orderliness or disarray of a scene can tell a lot about an event; however, the CSI must restrain from giving their opinion and must also describe only what they are seeing. A succinct description of a scene may be something such as:

> The scene consisted of a single-story, family home with three bedrooms, two bathrooms, a living room, and a kitchen. The drawers from all of the cabinets and dressers in all of the rooms were open and several were on the ground. There were papers strewn about the home, clothing on the floors, and the trash cans were knocked over.

In the above example, the CSI clearly indicates that the home was in disarray. Some readers may think an altercation, or a fight occurred,

DOI: 10.4324/9780429343162-3

or perhaps a robbery. It is also possible that this is "normal" in this house. Based on the description, however, the reader knows the house was not tidy. It is important to note that nowhere in this description is there an opinion. A CSI must never include their opinion when describing a location or event. The below is an opinionated example that CSIs should avoid:

> The location was a single-story, three-bedroom, two-bathroom house. It was obvious a fight had occurred since drawers were open and on the floor. The altercation occurred in every room of the house. There were clothes all over, indicating a struggle. Papers were strewn on the floors showing a burglary took place.

This example is highly opinionated, and many of these statements may prove to be false during the course of the investigation. A CSI must never make statements in their report that may prove false as the detectives investigate. This will lead to a contradiction in the case and can cause major issues in court.

Succinct writing is important in every aspect of the scene report, not just descriptions. When discussing weather conditions, scene processing, photos, videos, or any other portions of the report, clear-to-the-point statements will help the CSI get the point across plainly and factually.

Punctuation and Grammar

Proper grammar and punctuation are very important when writing a report. CSIs who struggle in these areas should look into online support tools such as Grammarly. Programs such as these will allow the CSI to see their errors and fix them immediately. Other options include having other investigators proofread or review their reports. In accredited crime scene investigation units, this administrative review will be required under the quality management system. All reports should be looked at by more than one person to ensure grammar, punctuation, and wording issues are addressed.

As previously mentioned, those reading reports will form an opinion about the writer immediately. Reports that are poorly organized, not clearly written, or with bad grammar and punctuation make the writer look uneducated, unprofessional, and disorganized. This may lead a reader to relate these qualities to their work as a CSI and cast doubt on the totality of their work. If the CSI cannot write a clear, concise, and organized report that is easy to understand, how skilled and organized are they as a CSI?

The organization and format of the report will vary depending on the requirements of the CSI's agency. No matter what the basic report structure is, CSIs should develop their own habits of writing that will help them remember important details when testifying. Writing item descriptions the same way every time or describing locations the same way will enable the CSI to develop a pattern that is easy to remember, understand, and testify to throughout their career. In today's day of technology, many CSIs are accustomed to using autocorrect and texting acronyms, abbreviations, and slang in their writing, and this translates into their report writing. CSIs should ensure that they are not writing in shorthand, slang, or abbreviations that a layperson will not understand. CSIs should also re-read their reports and make sure the autocorrect function has not corrected words in their report to words that were not intended.

Some common grammatical errors include but are not limited to:

THE WORD THAT CSI MEANT TO USE:	COMPUTER AUTOCORRECTED OR CSI TYPO TO:
Decedent	Descendant
Trial	Trail
Field	Filed

CSIs must also write reports in complete sentences. Many times, simple definite articles are left out of sentences, making the sentences incomplete or inaccurate. For example:

> Victim was found on the ground supine.

In this sentence, it is not clear to which victim the writer is referring. Adding a definite article, the word "the", in front of the word "victim" indicates to the reader that there is a specific victim who was found on the ground. While often acceptable in notes, many CSIs miss this important grammatical feature in their report writing, making their sentences inaccurate and hard to follow. The above sentence should be changed to:

The victim was found supine on the ground.

This reorganization of the sentence makes the description of the victim much clearer. The reader now knows there is a specific victim, and they know they are ***supine*** (lying on their back) on the ground. With a couple of words and grammatical corrections, the image is now much clearer.

CSI reports include a lot of data and specific details about items of evidence and processing. It is important that the CSI list items clearly and use the correct punctuation in their writing. Some CSIs will work for agencies that have them list out items of evidence in their report. The amount of detail that is required in the report may vary, but CSIs should maintain a very detailed list somewhere: their field notes, the chain of custody, or the report. If in the report the CSI is asked to list out the items of evidence, they should ensure they are listing them in brief, succinct statements which utilize correct punctuation. For example, if the CSI is listing that they collected one handgun, they should list this item as:

One (1) handgun, black in color, ...

Oftentimes, CSIs will list the above as:

One (1), handgun black in color ....

The placement of the comma in the sentence changes the meaning. The writer wants the reader to understand they recovered one handgun. This is best understood when writing it, as in the first example. The second example forces the reader to ask the question "one what?" because it is unclear that the one is referring to the handgun. This is a clear example of how punctuation can cause readers of a report to have more questions than answers when they finish reading. A CSI always wants their report to answer questions, not raise additional ones.

Acronyms

Acronyms are abbreviations for terms that are formed from the initial letters of words to create shortened versions of the word. CSIs should spell out acronyms before using them. Professionals in the criminal justice field use a lot of coded language, jargon, and acronyms that the layperson will not often understand. These terms are common to the author of the report and easily overlooked when writing reports. It is imperative that CSIs write out acronyms, at least the first time the acronym is used in the report, so the viewer can comprehend what is being said in the report. As mentioned earlier, CSI reports are highly technical and can get confusing. Using acronyms makes them more confusing; therefore, it is important to spell out and sometimes define acronyms. Here is a short list of some commonly used acronyms (see the glossary for additional terms):

ACRONYM	DEFINITION
CSI	Crime Scene Investigator
LEO	Law Enforcement Officer
ALS	Alternate Light Source
LOV	Latents of Value
NLOV	No Latents of Value
Sgt.	Sergeant
Lt.	Lieutenant
BPA	Bloodstain Pattern Analysis
GSR	Gunshot Residue

Terminology

CSIs use a variety of processes on a crime scene and in the lab. Although the CSI report is being read by individuals often unfamiliar with the correct terminology in this field, the CSI must ensure they are using the correct terms throughout their report. A current, thorough resource of forensic science terms is available through the Organization of Scientific Area Committees for Forensic Science (OSAC) of the National Institute of Standards and Technology (NIST) at https://www.nist.gov/osac/osac-lexicon. When using the terms, the CSI must be knowledgeable of the terms and why they chose them and be prepared to explain them in court. Often, members of the public, especially jurors, think they know what a CSI does, what they are capable of, and what technology they have access to from watching television shows. The CSI must be prepared to explain the reality of the job, the resources, the limitations, and the materials they have. CSIs must also be prepared to explain the differences between what they really did on a scene and how that may compare to what the readers of their reports have seen on television. For example, many readers believe a CSI can spray a chemical, and latent bloodstains will immediately begin to appear or fluoresce. The reality is the usage of this chemical depends on a lot of circumstances, such as lighting, surface type, make-up, and amount of blood, if there is blood at all present, and how the chemical is applied. When a CSI discusses the use of this chemical in their report, they must use the correct chemical terminology and then be prepared to explain this enhancement method and how it works in court. CSIs should not shy away from using the correct chemical terms for the processes they complete on a scene and in the lab. In fact, they should always use those terms consistently, but they should always be prepared to explain them in simple terms for a jury in court and for an investigator or other consumers of the CSI's report. Here is a short list of some commonly used terms (see the glossary for additional terms and the definitions of these terms):

TERMS
Cyanoacrylate or cyanoacrylate ester
Alternate light source
Rhodamine 6G
Luminol
Bluestar
Baseline coordinates
Triangulation
Trajectory
Impact angles
Bloodstain pattern analysis
Stringing

Summary

A basic understanding of the fundamentals of English writing is crucial in CSI report writing. CSIs must include facts and details in their reports but must do so in very specific statements with care taken to not include unsupported conclusions or opinions. If a CSI writes the facts of what they see clearly and succinctly, they will get the reader to understand the scene through their eyes. CSIs are scientists and use processes that most only understand or are familiar with through television. It is critical that a CSI explains the science and processes of the work they do in clearly defined sentences using the correct terms. Not only does this make their reports more accurate, but it also makes the CSI sound professional and well versed in their field.

End of Chapter Questions

1. Define succinct.
2. Define "decedent" and "descendant". What is the difference?
3. Clearly and succinctly describe a place you know very well.
4. Why is it important for a CSI to write succinctly?
5. What is an acronym and why should they be defined first?

Reference

https://www.merriam-webster.com/dictionary/succinct.

3

The Use of Field Notes and How to Document and/or Incorporate Notes into CSI Reports

LAURA PAZARENA

Field Notes

Field notes are notes that are taken by the investigator while on the scene or conducting processing in the lab. It is important that investigators learn how to take quick, concise field notes that they can interpret and understand. Field notes are generally not "pretty"; they are taken quickly and use a CSI's personal shorthand. There may be things crossed off and corrected, due to the complex nature of scenes and the vast amount of information a CSI receives from a variety of sources. The purpose of field notes is to remind the investigator of the details from the scene and the information they were given about the condition of the scene or items within it from other people upon their arrival. Similar to the report, the field notes should be written chronologically. Depending on when an investigator gets a call to respond to a scene, the order of their field notes may change. It is very important that the CSI annotates all times in their field notes: when they received the call or notice to go to the scene, when they arrived on the scene, when they began processing the scene, and when they cleared the scene. These become very important when creating a timeline of events in court. It is also important that the investigator is very clear on how they were notified: by cell phone, work phone, in person, or any other method. Again, this helps explain timelines and events in court. Field notes are very personal, and each investigator will learn their own shorthand writing and include information they

DOI: 10.4324/9780429343162-4

deem important from scene to scene. Generally speaking, field notes should minimally include:

- Date
- Time
- Weather
- Location
- Method of notification
- Who made the notification
- Type of case
- Initial briefing information upon arrival
- Scene events prior to CSI arrival
- Anomalies on the scene
- Rough sketch of the scene
- Measurements of physical evidence
- What the investigator observed
- Additional locations or processing requested and by whom

Date, Time, Weather, and Location

Timelines are critical when it comes to investigating crime scenes. Many cases involve different locations and events and may extend over several hours, days, or even weeks. The CSI must keep their notes, and their reports, very clear when it comes to the timeline of events. Documenting the date, time, weather, and location for each portion of an investigation is critical for writing chronologically and explaining the story in a clear and concise manner. Field notes should begin with the date and time the CSI received the call or notification to respond to the scene. Depending on the shift the CSI is working and the operations of their agency, these calls may come from a dispatcher via cell phone, via radio dispatch while on duty, or in person from a detective. No matter how the notification is made, the CSI should always begin their notes with the first contact made in reference to the case. This begins their involvement in the case, and their notes and report should continue until they conclude their involvement in the case, which is usually when they submit their physical evidence to the Evidence Unit or evidence and property room. A distinction must be made when mentioning "weather" and "location". The weather that the CSI wants to take note of is the weather at the actual crime scene at the time *they* arrive on the scene. The detective or person notifying the CSI may mention the weather at the time of the call, but since the CSI is not present to observe this weather, it is hearsay and should be included in the Overview of the report if it is relevant to the case. It is very important for the CSI to annotate the weather at the time they arrive on the scene and begin processing. Weather drastically impacts what techniques can be done on a scene, and it is important to clearly indicate the weather at the time of processing so that the reader can understand what was done, what wasn't done, and why (see Figure 3.1). When discussing locations, a CSI must be clear about every location they respond to and when. Many scenes involve several locations, and when CSIs move from one location to another, they should write in their field notes the date and time they go to a new location as well as the address of that new location (see Figure 3.2).

Notifications

CSIs may be notified to work scenes or process items in the lab through a variety of methods depending on their agency. Many agencies have an internal requesting system for detectives to request what is known as "in-house" processing or the processing of items that are already in the custody of the agency's Evidence Unit. This often occurs when agency members outside of the crime scene unit collect items of evidence from a scene without the aid of a CSI. Depending on the agency, crime scenes such as burglaries may be processed by

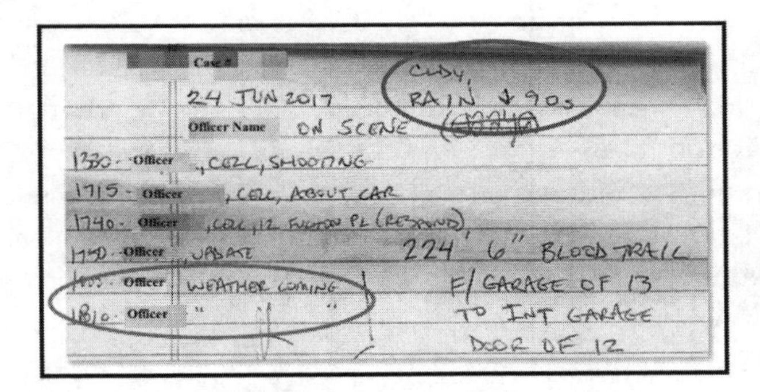

Figure 3.1 Field notes indicating the weather at the time the CSI arrived (circled in red) and the calls from initial responding officers on scenes indicating weather was coming (circled in blue). When this report is written, the CSI will put the weather they know for a fact (circled in red) under "Weather" and discuss the weather from the initial responders in the "Overview".

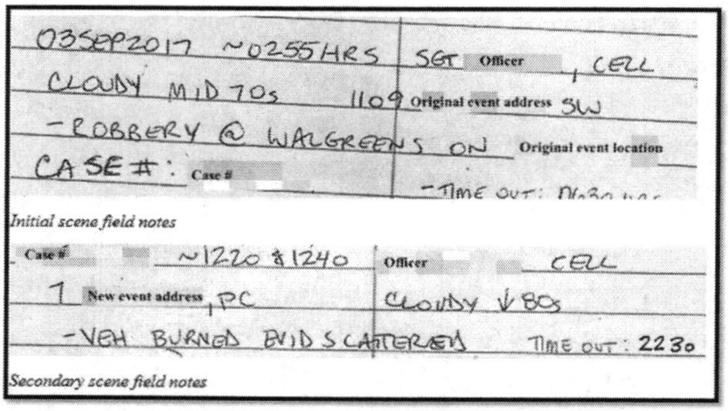

Figure 3.2 Field notes indicating one case with two different scenes. The top notes indicate the date, time, weather, location, notification, and case type for the initial call. The bottom notes indicate the same information for the secondary scene.

the initial responding officer or deputy and not a CSI. If the officer/deputy recovers evidence items such as crowbars, screwdrivers, or other physical materials from these types of scenes, they may ask for additional processing in the lab. These requests may be made through an internal agency requesting method, in person, by email, or by phone call (see Figure 3.3). No matter how the notification is made, the CSI must clearly indicate in their field notes – and their report – how they were notified of the request to process these items.

The same applies to notifications to respond to crime scenes. Depending on the agency, CSIs may be on-call or may work at an agency that operates with CSI staff on duty 24 hours a day. If a CSI is on-call, they will often receive phone calls from dispatchers or detectives via cell phone at home. If the CSI is on duty, they may receive the notifications in person or via radio dispatch. No matter how the notification is received, it is important to annotate the date, time, method of notification, and who the notifier was (see Figure 3.4). If dispatch notifies of a scene by phone, they may transfer the CSI to a detective or ask the CSI to call the officer or detective on the scene. If this occurs, the CSI should annotate they were transferred or they called, to whom they were transferred or called, and then what they are told (see Figure 3.5).

Type of Case and Initial Briefing Information

In the initial notification, the notifier may or may not tell the CSI what type of case they are being requested for. An initial part of the

EVIDENCE/PROPERTY PROCESSING/LAB REQUEST FORM

Request Date		Case #	

Item #	DESCRIPTION OF ITEM (Type, Make, Model, Color, Serial #, Marks, etc.)
Item 631.1	Red/Wht Mongoose Rebel Bicyle SN SNA0B

SYNOPSIS

FILL IN SYNOPSIS FOR PROCESSING REQUESTS AND/OR DNA FROM PROPERTY CRIMES ONLY
Synopsis: A description of the case, include how evidence submitted relates to case. Be specific on what processing is to be done:

Victim was operating his 2014 Chrysler 300, bearing Maryland tag while employed with Pizza Hut and was making a delivery to 52 Florida. Victim observed a black male juvenile riding a bicycle. Victim placed his vehicle in park, but left it running and unlocked as he approached the residence to make the pizza delivery. Victim stated when he got to the door, he observed the same male who was riding the bicycle, enter his vehicle and leave the area.

Bicycle to be processed for DNA and FP in areas where the suspect could have handled bicycle.

PROCESSING BEING REQUESTED

☐FA	☐Digital	☒DNA	☒FP

EMPLOYEE MAKING REQUEST: Signature: ______________ ID # Printed Name:

DNA CONSENT

The listed member of the Flagler County Sheriff's Office (FCSO) has properly identified themselves to me and has asked for my consent to retrieve a blood and/ or buccal swab from my person. I willingly and voluntarily give written consent to the member of the FCSO to obtain a blood and/or buccal swab from my person. I understand that this sample may be stored in a database for future comparisons. This form was signed by me without any threats and/or promises of any kind.

Signature:	Print Name:	Signature:	Print Name:
Signature:	Print Name:	Signature:	Print Name:
Signature:	Print Name:	Signature:	Print Name:

Figure 3.3 An agency in-house processing request form.

19 SEP 2017 ~0545 Notifying Officer - CELL
ATT. HOMICIDE 156 Address
PTLY CLDY ↓ 70s CASE: Case #
— Officer on scene ON SCENE - NO COMMENTS
— Officer on scene — SHOOTING IN DRIVEWAY
— SUSP/VICT MET IN DRIVEWAY
— VIDEO OF SUSP SHOOTING VICT
— VICT @ HOSP. + DIED

Figure 3.4 Field notes indicating the date, time, method of notification, and the notifier. In this case, the CSI was notified by the "Notifying Officer" on a cell phone. These notes also have an initial briefing of officers on the scene.

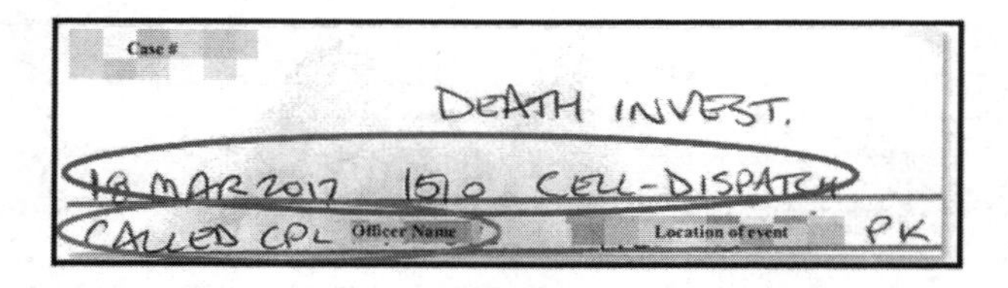

Figure 3.5 Field notes indicating the date and time the dispatcher called (circled in red) and then who the CSI called immediately after (circled in blue).

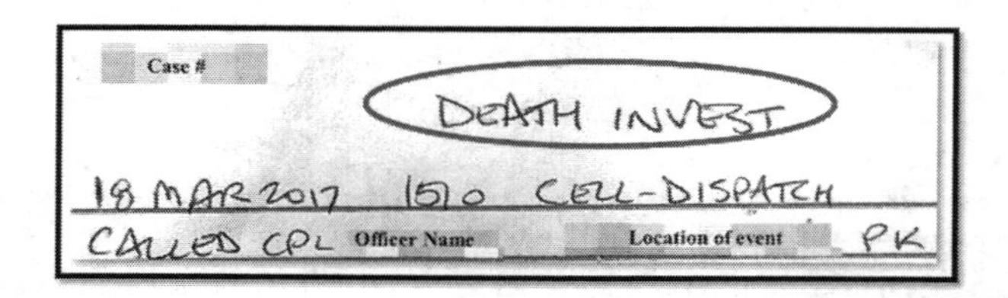

Figure 3.6 Field notes indicating the original case type stated by the notifier.

crime scene process is to assess the scene, and this begins with the notification. When the CSI is notified of the incident they want to ensure they annotate what type of case they are being told they are going to. This will allow the CSI to begin to assess the nature of the scene(s) and determine the equipment and materials needed and scene processing that may be required. Field notes should indicate the original case type that the notifier states (see Figure 3.6). CSIs should be aware the call they receive is rarely the call they get. This means a CSI may be told they are going to a specific type of scene and upon arrival find out it is much more, less, or completely different than originally thought. A homicide may initially be dispatched as an unconscious person, medical emergency, shooting, stabbing, or something else. It is always beneficial to have some idea of what a CSI may be walking into, therefore indicating the type of case is important for the notes and the report.

Upon arrival on the scene, there are often first responders from multiple agencies. The CSI must find a point of contact, usually a lead detective or supervisor, and get an initial briefing of the scene and investigation. As mentioned, what is received during the initial notification may be very different from what is actually happening on the scene. Continuing with our field note theme, the CSI must indicate the date and time they arrived at the scene and then indicate who they meet with and get briefed by. An ***initial briefing*** means an individual familiar with the scene and the case gives the CSI a quick explanation of what they know to this point. The brief generally includes what they know happened to lead to the event and what evidence they have found. The CSI is particularly interested in the physical evidence, and any processing that is being requested or they think may need to be done. The CSI should briefly and concisely write down what is said in the initial brief. Keep in mind, this is not word-for-word writing of what the briefing officer says, this is a quick summary to remind the CSI of what was said when writing the report (see Figure 3.7). The brief often occurs during a walkthrough. A ***walkthrough*** is when the officer/deputy/detective who is giving the initial brief literally walks the CSI through the scene and points out items of interest. This is when many physical items are explained and shown, such as bloodstains or cartridge casings, and additional processing may be requested. It is important to note these items in field notes as they are shown and discussed.

Anomalies and Observations

As the CSI does a walkthrough of the scene, items may be pointed out that they should be making a note of, but, as an expert, other items may stand out as important to the CSI. The officer may point out a cartridge casing, and then the CSI notices a defect in the floor. This defect may indicate there is a projectile nearby, meaning additional searching will need to be done after the brief. These are items that

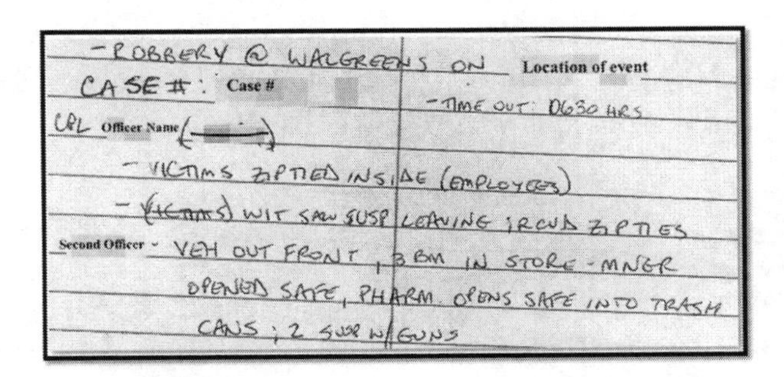

Figure 3.7 Field notes indicating an initial briefing. Notice there are some items crossed off and a lot of shorthand. As the CSI is briefed, they need to write fast and will often make errors that need to be corrected (crossed out, never erased) and learn their own way to shorten words to get the information in their notes quickly.

the CSI should write in their field notes at the time they are seen, so they remember to come back and look for the projectile or additional defects. ***Anomalies*** may include gunshots, bloodstains, latent blood, or a variety of other items or processes that the detective does or does not point out or recognize as significant. As mentioned in the introduction, CSIs are not trash collectors, and they bring unique experience, viewpoints, and expertise that are valuable to an investigation. The anomalies are often items or processes that the CSI will think of due to their experience and are often critical to a case. Making a note of them is important, so CSIs remember to come back to them later.

The anomalies are often a part of the observations a CSI makes on the scene. CSIs want to state only facts – things they know because they can see them, or they did them themselves. A CSI may observe a couch flipped over, drawers from all the dressers on the floor, papers thrown around a house, and food burned on the stove in a pot. These are facts, and they can be seen and photographed and clearly explained as being found this way. CSIs want to clearly indicate these conditions and observations in their notes and photograph them. A CSI should never say in their notes or reports any opinion drawn from these facts. Based on the above description, the reader would conclude that the house was messy or perhaps a struggle ensued while someone was cooking dinner, but nowhere in the CSI's notes or report should it state that a struggle ensued, or someone was cooking dinner. Those are not facts to the CSI, they were not present at the time and do not know if that's what happened, but by clearly noting their observations, the CSI will get the reader to understand what could have occurred in the location. Noting observations and items is one of the most important parts of the CSI's job, but the notes are objective – meaning without opinion (see Figure 3.8).

Scene Events before *CSI Arrival*

Having an understanding of the actions taken by other first responders and investigators before the arrival of the CSI will aid in the subsequent investigation. Any manipulation of the scene, including for medical or safety reasons, must be documented. Undocumented changes to the scene and items within it degrades the evidence, brings the agency's credibility into question, and may possibly negatively affect forensic analysis and admissibility of the physical evidence.

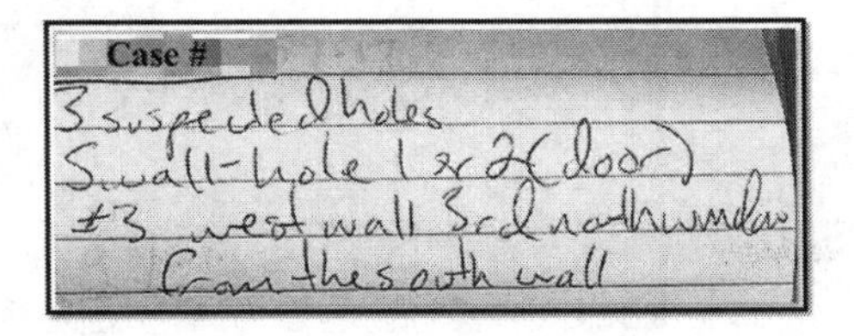

Figure 3.8 Field notes indicating anomalies (suspected gunshots) observed by the CSI during the walkthrough. These shots will need to be examined more by the CSI during their investigation. Notice the use of the word "suspected", CSIs must always remain objective in their descriptions.

If a shooting victim is moved from the initial location or position s/he was found in order to render medical aid, such a fact will likely be important when conducting a crime scene reconstruction of the incident. While important to an investigation and scene examination, the reports of emergency medical services (EMS) personnel do not include the location and position of the patient upon EMS arrival.

First responding deputies commonly move items within a scene to render medical care or for safety reasons but often fail to document such changes to the scene in their reports. For these reasons, it is important for CSIs to request information regarding any disruptions to the scene – or any items within it – from the condition found by initial responding officers. The CSI should make note of such information and request that the officers/deputies document their actions in their respective reports as well.

While recording the actions of others on the scene prior to the CSIs arrival may be hearsay for testimonial purposes, having such information can be crucial in conducting a thorough and informed scene examination. It is not uncommon for the first arriving officer or deputy to a shooting scene to disturb the scene by moving a firearm (whether out of curiosity, negligence, or for safety reasons) and also rendering the firearm safe (removing the magazine and any cartridges from the chamber). By documenting the actions of others and the rationale for the actions, alterations to the scene and items within it can be properly accounted for (see Figure 3.9).

Sketches and Measurements

In addition to documenting the scene through photography and field notes, a sketch of the scene should be completed including measurements for all physical items collected. A sketch of the crime scene,

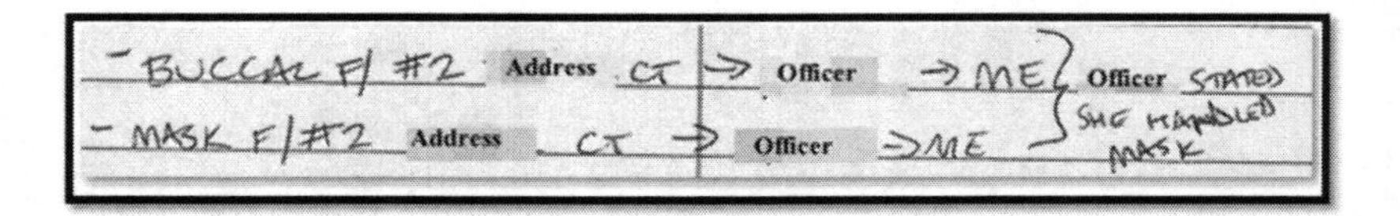

Figure 3.9 Field notes indicating that items were handled by initial responding officers.

together with other relevant documentation, should enable all items of potential evidentiary value to be located at the scene and the relation of such evidence items to other objects and evidence items. Sketching is used to specifically describe the location of items of potential evidentiary value in situ prior to collection, the location of items of potential evidentiary value relative to other objects present and other potential evidentiary items, and the physical scene.

In the field notes, CSIs should complete ***rough sketches***, which are hand-drawn sketches done on the scene to remind the CSI of the layout of the location, the location of the evidence, and the fixed points they used. These on-scene rough sketches do not need to be fancy, perfectly proportional, or include arrow-straight lines; they are simply a reminder to the CSI for when completing the final sketch, which will be pristine (see Figure 3.10).

Once a CSI leaves a scene, there is no returning to the scene as it was encountered; therefore, it is imperative to obtain all measurements required for any sketching, trajectory, and physical items. Depending on the measuring method, the types and number of measurements will change. CSIs will develop their own way of documenting measurements, but based on the author's experience, a good starting point is to write down the fixed points and create a table. A lot of CSIs use rectangular coordinate mapping for not-to-scale sketches. This includes two fixed points and one measurement from each point to the center mass of the physical item of evidence. The CSI should first determine the fixed points, making sure they have a north/south and an east/west point. A table can then be made to quickly annotate the measurements for each item. If working a scene as a solo CSI, it is often helpful to create this table and then get an officer on scene to help fill it in. Simply telling the officer where to write the numbers makes it easy to get help and easy for the CSI to understand what is in the table. Of note, when obtaining assistance from an officer, they may not put all data in the correct location. Always double-check the

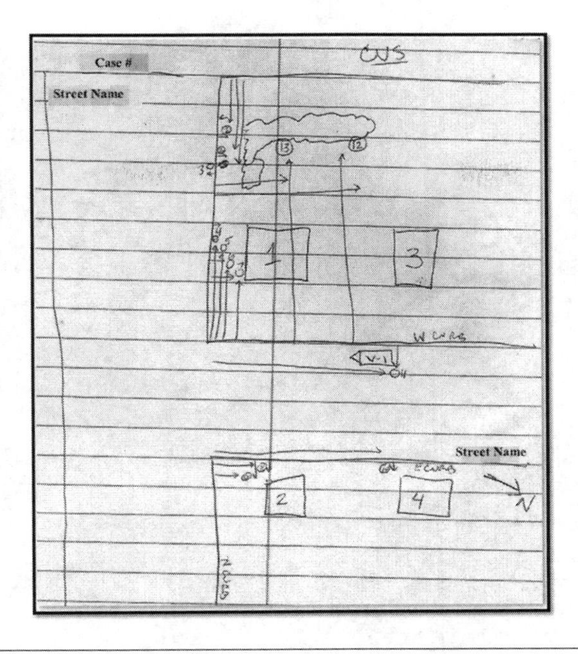

Figure 3.10 Rough sketch in field notes. These are not pristine, and a CSI does not need to be an artist. These are reminders for the CSI of items and fixed point locations to assist them when creating the final sketch.

information prior to departing the scene and correct any errors (see Figure 3.11).

For example, a CSI arrives at a scene, and they find three items in the living room of a home. During their processing, they would put photo placards by each item and in their notes clearly indicate what each photo placard is. When it comes time to measure, a table that indicates the number and the fixed points can be created, and all that is needed from the officer assisting is filling in the table with the measurements:

	FIXED POINT #1	FIXED POINT #2
PHOTO PLACARD	SOUTH OF NORTH WALL	EAST OF WEST WALL
1		
2		
3		

In the above table, the fixed points are the north wall and the west wall. The CSI would measure south of the north wall and east of the

Case #

	(Street) N OF N CURB	(Street) S OF N CURB	E OF W CURB	
1.	2			
2.	4"		51 (c/s Lot)	
3.		8"	69-4 73-2	
4.	4-4'			92-8
5.	6			94-4
6.	16-6			95-2
7.	27-2			90-4
8.	38-2		11'4"	
9.	32-8		12'2"	
10.	128-2		6"	
11.	131		9-4 (E of W curb)	
12.	113-8			171-8
13.	65-8			165-6

Figure 3.11 Field notes with table of measurements and fixed points. Notice there were some errors by the officer assisting and the CSI made notes to clarify. This is common and acceptable; the CSI wants to ensure everything is correct before leaving the scene.

	S OF N	E OF W.
1. 18' 4"	18'4"	13'
2.	6.58'	40.70'
3.	7.93'	8.85'
4.	3.10'	5.75'
5.	18.2'	4.78'

Figure 3.12 Field notes with a table showing placard numbers and fixed points.

west wall. When the CSI takes those measurements for each item, they could tell the officer to write the numbers in the applicable box of the chart. This will then give all measurements needed for the final report.

Tables are a quick way to set up field notes for measuring that can be used for any type of mapping method or trajectory (see Figure 3.12).

Additional Processing or Locations

Lastly, a CSI may find out that an investigation includes multiple scenes (locations) or other items of evidence that need processing. Inside the scene itself, additional, advanced processing may be requested. CSIs should annotate as soon as they find out about additional processing or locations and who told them about these items. Field notes may get jumbled since so many people give so much information at one time; therefore, it is imperative that the CSI keep the information clear and organized to enable the CSI to be able to chronologically write their report and process the other locations or complete the additional processing. As with anything else, noting who is asking for processing or communicating additional locations is important to the case.

Summary

Field notes may get mixed up and jumbled due to the complexity and chaos of the scenes. A lot of people give a lot of information in a short amount of time. The CSI should keep in mind the format of their agency report and how they are going to tell the final story when writing their field notes. Note-taking changes with experience, and CSIs will develop their own patterns and shorthand methods that work for them. Every agency has a different report style, and field notes are often adjusted based on the nature of the scene(s) and the processing required, but the information in this chapter should be included in notes, no matter what report format is being done. The CSI is ultimately the one that will need to testify to the work they did, so their notes need to make sense to them and include all of the information needed for the final report.

End of Chapter Questions

1. Define field notes.
2. What are the elements that should be included in field notes?
3. Define initial briefing.
4. Define walkthrough.
5. Define anomalies.
6. Why is the documentation of the date, time, weather, and location in field notes important?
7. What are rough sketches, and why are they completed?

4

When and How to Include Field Documentation Such as Photographs, Sketches, and Video in CSI Reports

LAURA PAZARENA

Photographs

Crime scene investigators should photograph everything they do in addition to thoroughly photo-documenting the scene. All crime scenes, evidence, and processing should be photographed, and this should be done before, during, and after alterations. Thorough, unaltered photographs are critical to cases and CSIs must ensure proper photographic documentation. The sequence and protocols for photographing will differ from agency to agency and even from CSI to CSI, but the final crime scene report should always include a section about photographs.

Before digital photography, CSIs were required to keep a photo log and some agencies continue their use today. A ***photo log*** is a list of every single photo that was taken, the settings on the camera, and what the photo depicts. This was very important when CSIs were using film photography since the images could not be seen immediately. Modern-day photography is almost 100% digital; therefore a CSI can view the images and the metadata immediately. This ability to view the images as soon as they are taken has lessened the need for a photo log.

What has become very important for modern photography is where and how the photos are stored. Depending on the agency and their

DOI: 10.4324/9780429343162-5

standard operating procedures, they may use a database system managed by a third party or they may create their own secure network for digital images. There are numerous companies that offer secure databases for the storage of digital images. What is important for the CSI is a clear understanding of where the photos are being stored and how they can be retrieved for investigating officers, tendering to legal parties during discovery, and ultimately for court. In the report, the CSI should always state how many total images were taken for the case and the exact location the images can be found. Oftentimes this can be a copy of the link or the name of the database. This is crucial for court purposes. Attorneys need to know how many images exist and where they can be found so they can make the proper request for prosecution purposes (see Figure 4.1).

Sketches

When a CSI is required to complete a crime scene sketch will depend on the policies and procedures of their agency. The specifics that are required on the sketch will also depend on the agency. Whenever a sketch is completed, the CSI should always document in their report how many sketches were done, who completed the sketch(es), and where the sketch(es) may be found. Sketches should be separate documents and not a part of the body of the report. Similar to photos, the investigators and attorneys must know exactly where to find the sketch; therefore it is imperative that the CSI lists the sketch or sketches in the report and where they can be found (see Figure 4.2).

It is important to note that the way sketches are completed may differ from CSI to CSI and agency to agency; however, when a sketch is done there are five elements that should always be included on the sketch itself. All of these elements should be in the margins of the sketch, not in the diagram area:

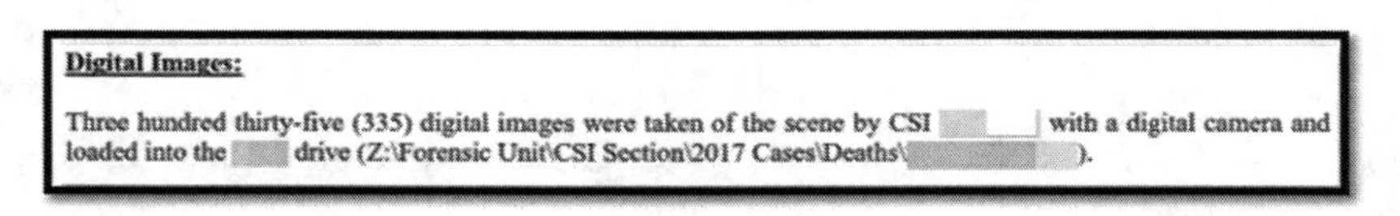
Digital Images:

Three hundred thirty-five (335) digital images were taken of the scene by CSI [redacted] with a digital camera and loaded into the [redacted] drive (Z:\Forensic Unit\CSI Section\2017 Cases\Deaths\[redacted]).

Figure 4.1 This statement would be in the final CSI report and clearly indicates how many total images were taken, what they are of, who took them, and where they can be found.

Diagram:

A diagram of the scene was completed by CSI [redacted] (not to scale) and loaded into the [redacted] drive (Z:\Forensic Unit\CSI Section\2017 Cases\Deaths\[redacted]).

Figure 4.2 This statement would be in the final CSI report and clearly indicates how many sketches were done, who did them, and where they can be found.

1. **Title Block** – This is the "who, where, when" of the event. The CSI should annotate on the sketch who created the sketch, where the event took place, the date the CSI responded to the location, and the case number for the event. The title block typically includes (see 1. in Figure 4.5):
   - Case number
   - Crime/case type
   - Name and ID# of sketcher
   - Location of sketch
   - Date completed
2. **Header** – This is the "why" of the sketch. Near the top of the sketch document, there should be a simple statement telling the jury why the sketch was created (see 2. in Figure 4.5).
   a. For example: "Elevation sketch of the north bedroom wall".
3. **North Directional and Scale** – The CSI must indicate on the sketch which way north is. This is an imperative piece of the sketch so that the report and the sketch will match. The CSI should also annotate if the sketch is "to scale" or "not to scale" – some agencies even require final "to scale" sketches to be marked "not to scale" to alleviate any potential difficulties due to miscalibrations in the printed sketch. Most CSIs do "not to scale" sketches, which means the boxes or images in the sketch do not equal an exact measurement. Experts such as bloodstain pattern analysts and firearms examiners may create "to scale" sketches. In a "to scale", sketch items will be drawn out with measurements to indicate the exact size – for example, 1 inch equals 20 feet. "To scale" sketches can be complicated and time-consuming, but extremely important for crime scene reconstruction (see 3. in Figure 4.5).

4. **Legend** – This is a key to any and all symbols being used on the diagram. All physical items that were marked with placards and collected by the CSI should be annotated in the sketch with the placard number. Little symbols on a sketch, such as a small gun or cartridge casing, are confusing to a jury and cannot be correlated back with the report. Therefore, symbols should be avoided, and placard numbers should be used. The legend should match the sketch *exactly*. The legend will identify what items the numbers (placards) relate to. This should match the report and the photos. It is very important that CSIs ensure the consistency of their reports, photos, sketches, and chain of custody. Any other items in the sketch that are not obvious should also be labeled on the diagram or placed in the legend. Nothing should be left for a reader to "guess", and everything should be clearly labeled and defined in the legend or on the diagram (Figures 4.3 and 4.4; see 4. in Figure 4.5).
5. **Diagram** – The last element is the picture itself. The CSI must include an actual drawing on the sketch. The drawing should be clear and professional. Most agencies utilize computer programs for sketching; however, there may be times when sketches will need to be hand-drawn. If a sketch is hand-drawn, the CSI should use rulers, stencils, and bold dark lines to ensure the drawing is clear, understandable, and visible (see 5. in Figure 4.5).

All of the above elements for a sketch should be on a separate sketch document. None of these elements needs to be listed in the report. However, the report should match these elements exactly. The CSI must ensure that the north directional in the sketch matches the words for the measurements they write in the report. As mentioned previously, agencies have different policies for sketch creation. The author has tried a variety of sketching methods and has found that adding measurements to a bird's eye view sketch is very confusing and makes the sketch illegible, hard to understand, and difficult to explain. To remedy this, the author suggests not putting measurements on a sketch, but instead listing them in the recovery location for the items in the report. This will be discussed more in Chapter 4.

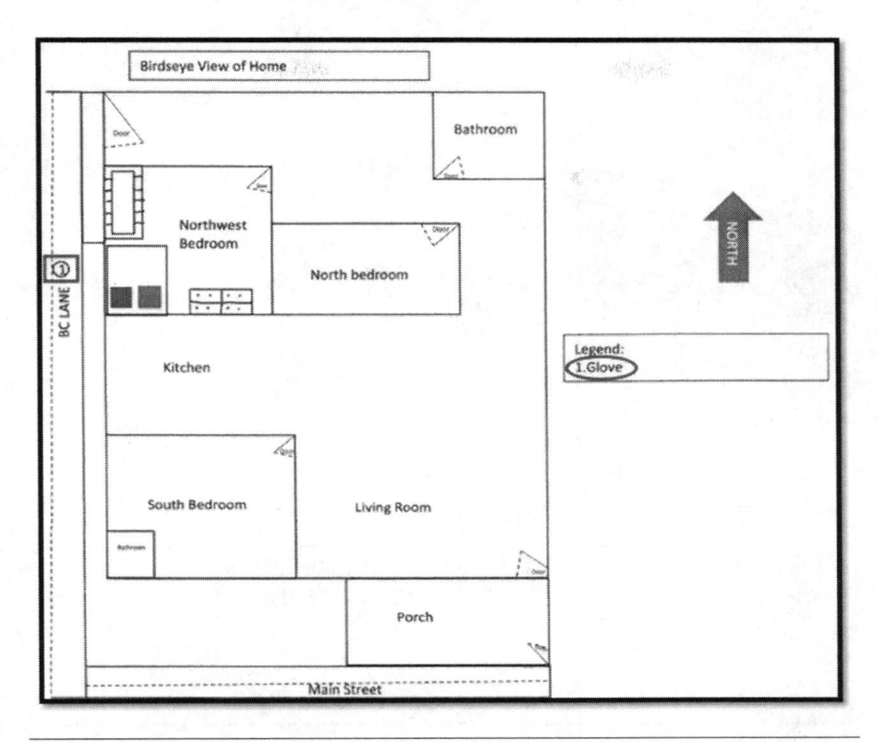

Figure 4.3 In this sketch, the item in the diagram is depicted as ③ and in the legend, it is 1., although this is a minor difference, these do not match and could lead a jury to wonder what item ③ is and where item 1. is in the diagram. In addition, there are a variety of different boxes and symbols on the diagram that are not clear, and these items should be labeled directly on the sketch or listed in the legend.

Video

Policing has changed dramatically over the last several years. Technology has been introduced and the way video can be done on scenes has expanded. Many agencies still utilize a standard video camera when they need to video a scene. Other options such as video features on a digital camera or police officer body-worn camera may also be implemented. When a video is taken will depend on the agency, but it is often useful when someone involved in the case is walking a CSI through the events at the location, or if a location is very large to help give a complete understanding of the scene.

When using video, a CSI should use care to not move too fast and should keep the microphone on mute after doing an introduction. Video documentation in the report is similar to photographs and

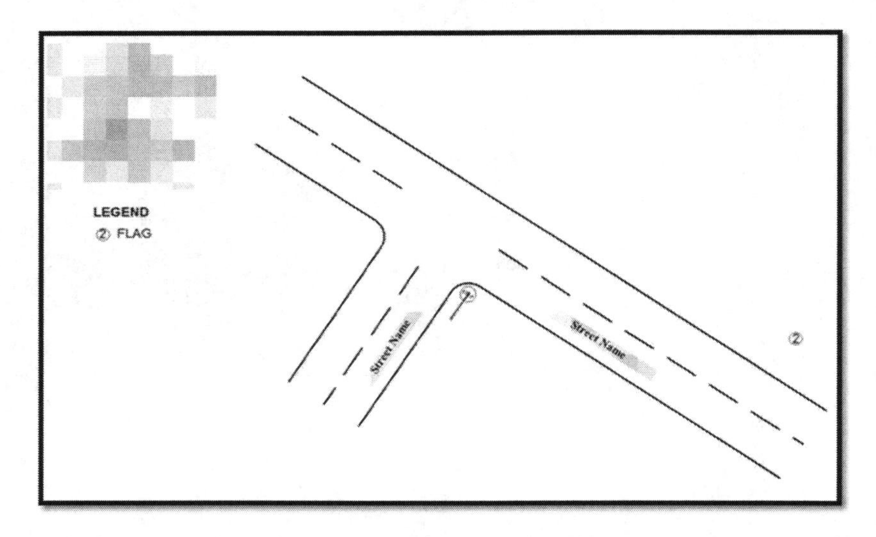

Figure 4.4 In this sketch, the legend and the item in the diagram have the same symbol, and the stop sign, and the streets are labeled directly on the diagram. This leaves nothing for a jury to question and make it clear what every item is.

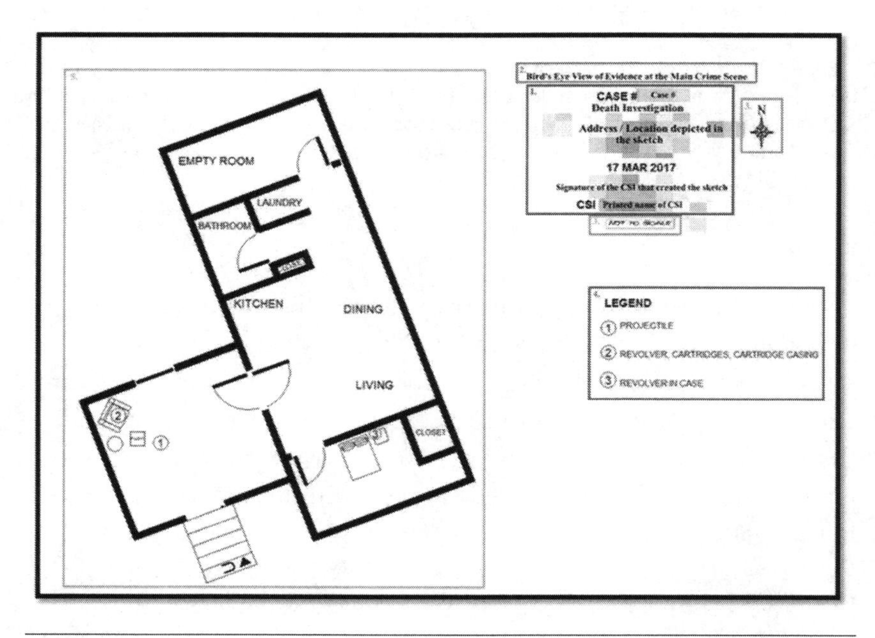

Figure 4.5 A complete sketch with all required elements. 1. Title block, 2. Header, 3. North directional and "Not to Scale", 4. Legend, 5. Diagram. Notice all the elements are in the margins of the sketch, not on the diagram.

Video:

A video of the scene was completed by CSI [redacted] using a Cannon handheld video camera. The video was loaded into the [redacted] drive (Z:\Forensic Unit\CSI Section\2017\ [redacted])

Figure 4.6 This statement would be in the final CSI report and clearly indicates how the video was taken, who took the video, and where the video can be found.

sketches and only needs to be a simple statement identifying the person who took the video, what the video was of, and where to find the video (see Figure 4.6).

Summary

A CSI will complete a variety of documentation on the scene and must include all of this information in the report. It is important the CSI includes how much documentation was done, who completed the documentation, and where it can be found. These details will become imperative if, and when, the case goes to court. CSIs must ensure that their reports match their other documentation such as photos and sketches; any discrepancies could cause issues in court, and therefore a CSI should be diligent in their consistency in all of their documentation.

End of Chapter Questions

1. Define a photo log.
2. State and define the five elements of a sketch.
3. Draw a sketch of a place you know very well.
4. Imagine you are a CSI responding to the place you sketched in question 2. You photograph the scene and complete a sketch. Write the digital images and diagram portion of the report based on your response to this location.

SECTION 2

Investigative Report Writing

5

General Guidelines for Writing CSI Reports for Crime Scenes

LAURA PAZARENA

Introduction

CSIs must document and record everything they do for a case. Crime scene investigation is such an important part of the investigative, forensic science, and judicial processes that most agencies develop a dedicated CSI Unit to undertake the processing of crime scenes. When responding to crime scenes, CSIs must ensure thorough documentation of the crime scene, the evidence, and, as it may alter or destroy physical evidence, describe any processing that they do on scene. Crime scene documentation is not only used for court but also often utilized by other experts to help them with the interpretation of the scene and the evidence. CSIs should make their reports easy to follow and understand while still explaining the technical work that they completed. CSIs should write the report chronologically to help the reader follow the timeline of the CSIs involvement in the case. Report writing requirements will vary from agency to agency, but the guidelines provided here will help the CSI learn a format and writing methodology that will help them when testifying in court. These guidelines may be adapted and applied to any report template at any agency.

Report Components

The CSI report should be written chronologically and should begin with how the CSI was notified that their assistance is needed and should end with the CSI's last involvement in the case, generally the

DOI: 10.4324/9780429343162-7

submission of the evidence. There are general components of a CSI report that should always be included:

- Case Information
    - Every report should include the case information. This information should include the case number, the address of the crime scene (or the location a vehicle or person was processed), the date and time of arrival and processing, the CSI's name and identification number, the type of case, and the names of the people involved if known. The author has found that having this information in a table at the top of the report is the easiest way for the CSI and future readers (such as law enforcement officers, attorneys, or expert witnesses) to reference the material (see Figure 5.1).
- Case Overview
    - The report should begin with a chronological overview of the case. The first portion should begin with the notification, how did the CSI get involved in this case? The CSI should clearly indicate when they were notified, how they were notified, and by whom they were notified. The overview should then continue with the CSI's response to the scene, who they met on the scene, and a summary of the initial brief and walkthrough. The walkthrough and initial brief should be summarized in the field notes. The CSI must now professionally explain in the report what they summarized in the notes. The overview is not verbatim; this is the CSI's understanding of what was said to them on the scene. It is important to note that this and an autopsy summary are the only times a CSI should include hearsay. ***Hearsay*** is information that a CSI is told from someone else that they did not personally observe. The information a CSI includes here explains why the CSI was involved and

<table>
<tr><td>CASE NUMBER:</td><td>CSI:</td><td>DATE (of the incident):</td><td>DATE (of processing):</td><td>APPROX. TIME (of processing):</td></tr>
<tr><td colspan="2">COMPLAINANT, VICTIM, WITNESS, DECEDENT, SUSPECT:</td><td colspan="2">INCIDENT::</td><td>APPROX. TIME (on the scene)</td></tr>
<tr><td colspan="4">LOCATION OF INCIDENT:</td><td>APPROX. TIME (depart scene)</td></tr>
</table>

Figure 5.1 Example of case information formatted in a table. This would be placed at the top of the report.

Case Overview:

On day of week and full date, at approximately 0910 hours, Sergeant notifying officer's name made contact with Crime Scene Investigator (CSI) , via cellphone, to request assistance at the above listed location in reference to a Commercial Burglary. Sergeant advised that the front door of the business was shattered in, possibly with a rock paver located on scene, and that a register with approximately $200 dollars was taken. On scene, contact was made with Deputy , who stated that the only thing confirmed missing by the manager on scene, was a register from the front counter. The following services were performed:

Figure 5.2 Example of a case overview. Notice the hearsay information being told to the CSI when notified and when arriving on the scene.

how the investigation started. After the overview portion of the report, the CSI should not mention any hearsay. The remainder of the report should be facts based on what the CSI personally did and saw (see Figure 5.2).

- Weather
    - Weather is an essential detail for a CSI when responding to a crime scene. The weather can help explain the condition of the scene and evidence, but it will also dictate what a CSI may or may not be able to do on a scene as well as the order of processing. As previously mentioned, the CSI should be documenting factual observations and only stating what they know to be true. Therefore, the weather on the crime scene prior to the CSI's arrival is hearsay and should not be included in this section. If the weather at the time of notification is important to the case, the CSI may mention it in the overview. In this section, the CSI should only indicate the weather on the crime scene at the time they arrived at the scene to process. This is the weather that the CSI is physically working in and this is the weather that dictates the processing of the scene. If the weather changes while the CSI is on scene and such changes in scene conditions cause the CSI to deviate from their processing, they should indicate the changes in their report. The statement about the weather can be a one-sentence summary indicating the approximate temperature and visibility at the time of processing. As discussed later, observations that may implicitly relate to weather events that may have occurred prior to the CSI's arrival on the scene may be mentioned in other sections of the CSI report when documenting the condition of the scene

(e.g., one inch of light powder snow was observed on top of the victim's body, the ground beneath and around the victim's body was wet, and the victim's outer clothing and shoes were wet).

- Examples:
  - Clear skies, approximately 95 degrees Fahrenheit.
  - Upon arrival, it was mostly cloudy and approximately 90 degrees Fahrenheit. During processing, thunderstorms began, and the temperature dropped to 75 degrees.

- Vehicle
  - A CSI will often respond to scenes that have several vehicles on scene. Often, not all of the vehicles are essential to the case, and they do not all need to be listed in the report. The vehicles listed should be those that are directly involved or collected. This may include vehicles that are recovered by the CSI for future processing or vehicles that are processed and remain on the scene (see Figure 5.3a). Scenes that involve multiple vehicles should be thoroughly

Vehicle:

V1: 2007 Honda, Ridgeline, burgundy in color, four door truck
Tag: NUMBER & STATE
VIN: ENTIRE VEHICLE ID NUMBER

V2: 2011 Dodge, Ram 1500, red in color, four door truck
Tag: NUMBER & STATE
VIN: ENTIRE VEHICLE ID NUMBER

5.3a: Vehicles that were not itemized and collected, but were important to the case.

Vehicle:

Item #405.1: 2008, Chevrolet, Suburban, white in color
Tag: NUMBER & STATE
VIN: ENTIRE VEHICLE ID NUMBER

5.3b: Vehicle was itemized and collected.

Figure 5.3 Examples of how to list vehicles in a report. Note all the identifying features of the vehicles are present and easily found. In 5.3a, the vehicles were not given item numbers, meaning they were not collected by the agency. In 5.3b, the vehicle has an item number indicating this vehicle was taken as evidence.

photographed and the vehicles should be documented through photos, but only the vehicles the CSI is directly involved with need to be listed in the report. An important detail to note is that *any* item a CSI collects and takes with them should be itemized, including vehicles (see Figure 5.3b). If a CSI tows a vehicle to their Evidence Unit, they must give the vehicle an item number for future reference. When listing the vehicle in the report, the CSI must include this item number and note if the vehicle was collected as evidence, so it can be correlated with the chain of custody and the vehicle itself. Vehicles should be listed with all identifying features. This includes license plate, vehicle identification number (VIN), make, model, color, and the number of doors. Any damage to the vehicle should be discussed in the Investigator's Notes section of the report. The vehicle section is a quick reference for the reader to know if any vehicles were processed or recovered (see Figure 5.3).

- Diagram
  - As mentioned in previous chapters a CSI is responsible for completing diagrams or sketches on certain scenes. When a diagram is completed is dependent on the agency's protocols. Whenever a CSI completes a diagram, they need to annotate in the report a diagram was done, who did the diagram, how many diagrams were created, what they are of, and where they can be found. The diagram(s) will be submitted as separate stand-alone documents. This portion of the report is a statement to let the reader know that there are diagrams that were completed (see Figure 5.4).
- Digital Images and Video
  - The digital images and video sections are similar to the diagram section. These sections should include statements

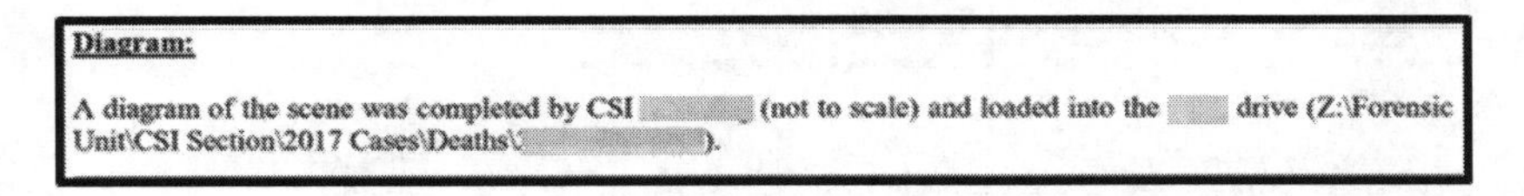
Diagram:

A diagram of the scene was completed by CSI [redacted] (not to scale) and loaded into the [redacted] drive (Z:\Forensic Unit\CSI Section\2017 Cases\Deaths\[redacted]).

Figure 5.4 This statement would be in the final CSI report and clearly indicates how many sketches were done, who did them, and where they can be found.

to tell the reader how many images or videos were taken, of what, by whom, and where they can be found. Again, these will be submitted separately and are mentioned in the report to advise the reader that they exist and should be included in materials requested and tendered for court purposes (see Figure 5.5).

- Items of Evidence
  - The Items of Evidence section, also commonly known as an evidence log, is one of the most important parts of the report. The author has found that listing the items in a very specific way helps when testifying in court, especially when several hundred items have been recovered. The guidance here will assist CSIs to understand what may be asked of them in court when testifying about the evidence. The way an agency guides a CSI to write the items may differ, but a CSI should remember that they will be the ones that need to testify to what they recovered. The CSI should always ensure that no matter how they document the items of evidence they recovered, they must be able to easily find and recall what they collected and from where.
  - Generally speaking, when describing items of evidence, the details the CSI should include are the following:
    - Item number – every single item a CSI collects, including vehicles, should be given a unique item number. This number must be different from any other items in the same case and is the number used to locate this piece of evidence in storage. Every agency itemizes evidence differently, but a CSI should make sure that all items collected and submitted on a case are given

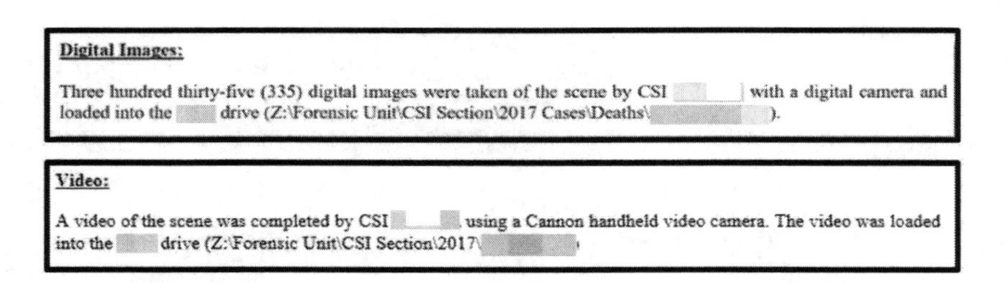

Digital Images:

Three hundred thirty-five (335) digital images were taken of the scene by CSI [redacted] with a digital camera and loaded into the [redacted] drive (Z:\Forensic Unit\CSI Section\2017 Cases\Deaths\[redacted]).

Video:

A video of the scene was completed by CSI [redacted] using a Cannon handheld video camera. The video was loaded into the [redacted] drive (Z:\Forensic Unit\CSI Section\2017\[redacted]

Figure 5.5 Examples of how to write digital images and video in the final report.

unique numbers to allow them to locate the evidence later (see 1. in Figure 5.8).

- Photo placard number – photo placards are the numbers set out on a scene next to a physical item of evidence that is going to be collected by a CSI. The use of placards will vary from agency to agency, but generally, placards are used next to items that are *physically being collected* (see 2. in Figure 5.8). Items such as tire impressions, foot impressions, and blood should be marked using rulers or other identifiers to document scale or size (see Figure 5.6). An important note about photo placards is that not every single item will have a photo placard. For example, on the scene, a fully loaded revolver might be labeled as Photo Placard #01(see Figure 5.7a), but when the CSI recovers the weapon and unloads it, the weapon becomes multiple items: the revolver and the cartridge casings, and cartridges from the cylinder (see Figure 5.7b). The same happens when a CSI recovers bags of drugs. On the scene, the entire bag is a photo placard, but when submitted it breaks down into the bag and the drugs.
- Quantity – this should be the number of items in the envelope or package that is submitted to the Evidence Unit (see 3. in Figure 5.8).

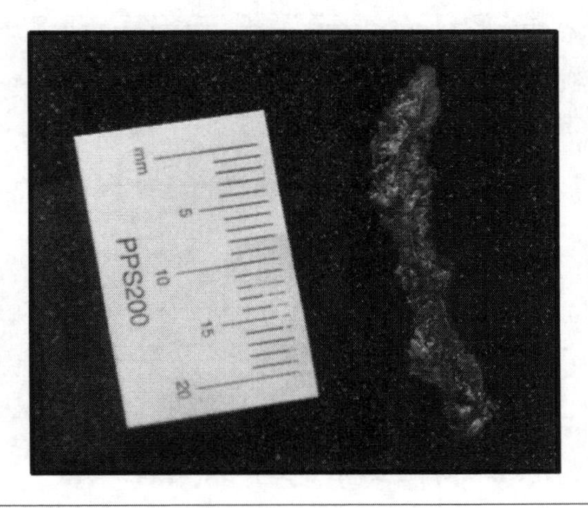

Figure 5.6 Example of rulers next to a bloodstain.

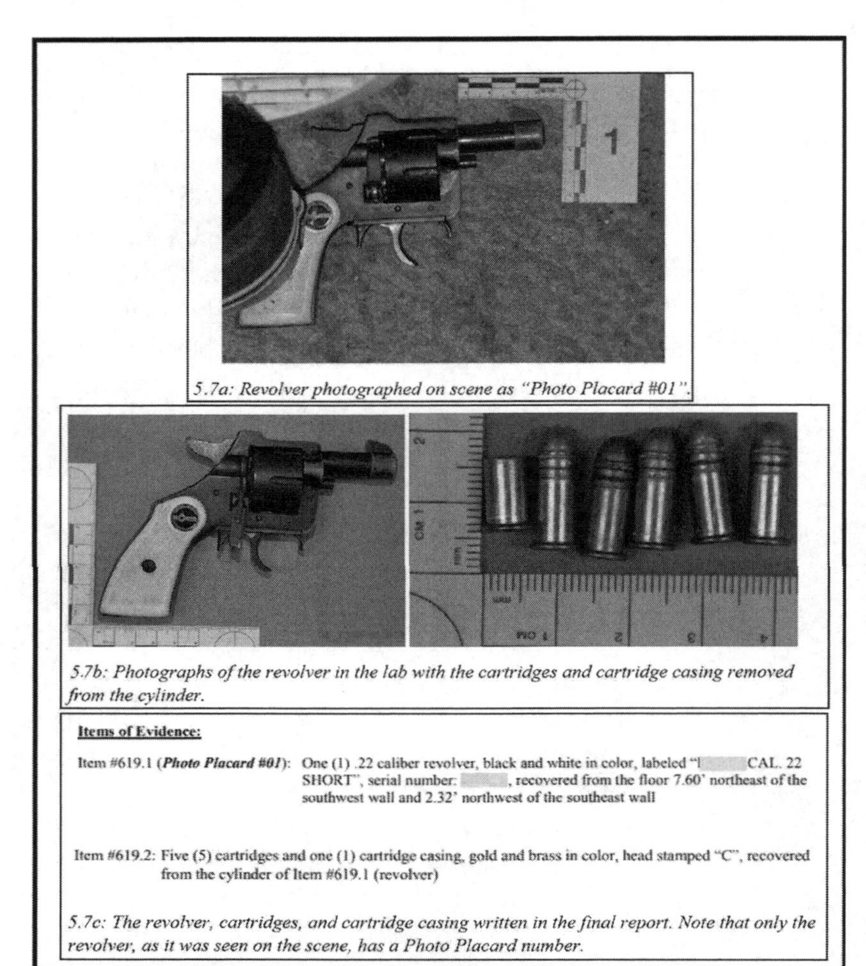

5.7a: Revolver photographed on scene as "Photo Placard #01".

5.7b: Photographs of the revolver in the lab with the cartridges and cartridge casing removed from the cylinder.

Items of Evidence:

Item #619.1 (***Photo Placard #01***): One (1) .22 caliber revolver, black and white in color, labeled "I[redacted] CAL. 22 SHORT", serial number: [redacted], recovered from the floor 7.60' northeast of the southwest wall and 2.32' northwest of the southeast wall

Item #619.2: Five (5) cartridges and one (1) cartridge casing, gold and brass in color, head stamped "C", recovered from the cylinder of Item #619.1 (revolver)

5.7c: The revolver, cartridges, and cartridge casing written in the final report. Note that only the revolver, as it was seen on the scene, has a Photo Placard number.

Figure 5.7 Example of an item labeled with a photo placard on the scene that contains other items, broken down, and then written correctly in the report.

- Item description (what the item is) – the proper names and terms for items must be used at all times. CSIs must be prepared to explain items to a jury that are not common terms. One of the most misused terms is "bullet". This term has a different definition to different people and a CSI must make sure they are using the correct term for the items they are recovering to eliminate confusion (see 4. in Figure 5.8).
- Color of the item – a general color should be included when describing items. CSIs want to ensure they are

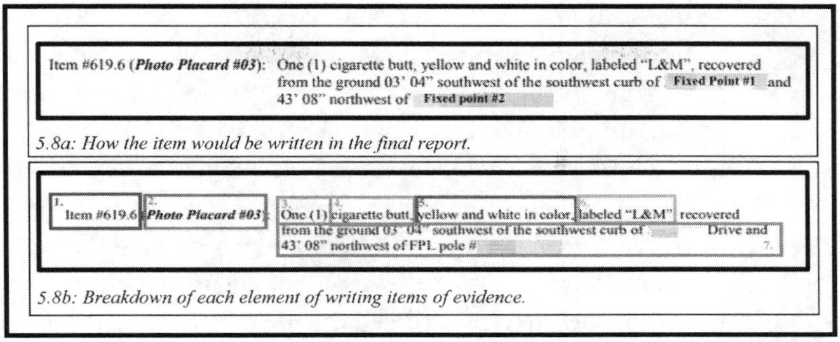

Item #619.6 (***Photo Placard #03***): One (1) cigarette butt, yellow and white in color, labeled "L&M", recovered from the ground 03' 04" southwest of the southwest curb of **Fixed Point #1** and 43' 08" northwest of **Fixed point #2**

5.8a: How the item would be written in the final report.

1. Item #619.6 2. ***Photo Placard #03*** 3. One (1) 4. cigarette butt, 5. yellow and white in color, 6. labeled "L&M" recovered from the ground 03' 04" southwest of the southwest curb of Drive and 43' 08" northwest of FPL pole # 7.

5.8b: Breakdown of each element of writing items of evidence.

Figure 5.8 An example of how to write an item of evidence with all the necessary information: 1. Item number, 2. Photo Placard number, 3. Quantity, 4. Item description, 5. Color, 6. Labels, 7. Recovery location – including fixed points.

not using terms such as a "gold necklace" because they do not in fact know the necklace is gold. This is a very important element of describing items. CSIs do not want to be held responsible for "gold" or "silver" jewelry when the items are not really gold or silver. Color can be a difficult descriptor since everyone sees color differently. CSIs want to use terms such as "gold in color", "gold-colored", "yellow metal", or "appeared to be yellow" to maintain factuality and details (see 5. in Figure 5.8).

- Labels/identifying features – most items have some manufacturer's labeling or markings on them, and a CSI should indicate them if they are observed. Some items, such as projectiles, may have no labelings. If items have no labels or markings, the CSI may exclude this portion of the description. Whenever possible, CSIs want to include at least the make, model, and serial number of items they recover. This is critical for items such as firearms that could be linked to several crimes or to the owner by serial number. CSIs do not need to list out every single word written on an item, but they do want to include the basics that will help individually to identify the item of interest and also aid investigators and evidence custodians in locating owners (see 6. in Figure 5.8).
- Recovery location – CSIs must be specific about where items were recovered. There are several mapping

methods that may be used on a crime scene when recovering evidence and CSIs will have multiple measurements to exactly locate items within the scene. Measurements on a sketch can make a sketch overwhelming and convoluted. It is the experience of the author that putting measurements on a crime scene sketch for every recovered item makes the sketch hard to read and hard for the CSI to explain to attorneys and, if the sketch is utilized during court proceedings, to a judge or jury. The measurements are still critical to the case and must be included. Listing the measurements in the description of the item in the report helps the CSI and the reader know exactly where the items were recovered and then correlate them with the sketch without overwhelming the sketch with measurements. The recovery location should include all measurements and where the item was found, such as on the ground or on a dresser, and in which room (see 7. in Figure 5.8).

- Prints and Swabs
    - When a CSI goes to court the jury usually wants to know if there were any fingerprints or DNA recovered in a case. Since these are two items that are most frequently requested in court the CSI should separate these into their own section in the report. These sections should list the physical fingerprint cards or swabs that a CSI collected. This section should also be where the CSI indicates if prints were developed on an item and photographed (see Figure 5.9b). The physical fingerprint cards and swabs are listed exactly like other items of evidence and should be given item numbers. Not all cases will have recovered prints and swabs. If a CSI does not collect any prints or swabs these sections should be listed as "N/A" (not applicable), but they should not be removed from the report. By indicating "N/A" the CSI will know when testifying that no prints or swabs were recovered. This is an easy way to quickly glance at the report and know whether or not these types of items were recovered. When listing prints and swabs it is imperative that the CSI state exactly where

Prints:

Item #515.2: One (1) manila envelope containing Latent Prints #01-03, labeled as follows:

LP #01: One (1) latent print card recovered from the middle of the left hand side of the register monitor
LP #02: One (1) latent print card recovered from the top right hand side, near corner, of the register monitor
LP #03: One (1) latent print card recovered from the top right corner of the register monitor

5.9a: Example of how to write recovered fingerprint cards in a report.

Prints:

Item #515.5: One (1) envelope containing latent prints #01-09, labeled as follows:

LP #01: One (1) latent print recovered from the interior driver's side front door window of Item #673.1 (Pontiac)
LP #02: One (1) latent print recovered from the interior driver's side front door window of Item #673.1 (Pontiac)
LP #03: One (1) latent print recovered from the interior driver's side front door window of Item #673.1 (Pontiac)
LP #04: One (1) latent print recovered from the front driver's side door jamb of Item #673.1 (Pontiac)
LP #05: One (1) latent print recovered from the rear view mirror of Item #673.1 (Pontiac)
LP #06: One (1) latent print recovered from the rear view mirror of Item #673.1 (Pontiac)
LP #07: One (1) latent print recovered from the interior passenger side front door window of Item #673.1 (Pontiac)
LP #08: One (1) latent print recovered from the interior passenger side front door window of Item #673.1 (Pontiac)
LP #09: One (1) latent print recovered from the interior passenger side front door window of Item #673.1 (Pontiac)

Several latent prints were developed on Item #515.3 utilizing ninhydrin.

5.9b: Example of how to list prints that were developed with ninhydrin. These prints remain on the item; therefore, no physical item fingerprint cards were recovered, and no item number is included. Note that they are still listed under the Prints Section of the report to allow the CSI to quickly reference them during court.

Item #619.3: One (1) manila envelope containing Swab #01, labeled as follows:

Swab #01: One (1) swab from the exterior edges and base of Item #619.1 (television)

5.9c: Example of how to write recovered swabs in a report.

Figure 5.9 Examples of how to write prints and swabs in the final report.

each was recovered. This becomes very important in court when attorneys try to link individuals to specific items of evidence (see Figure 5.9).

- Investigator's Notes
  - The Investigator's Notes are the bulk of the CSI report. This is the section where the CSI explains from beginning to end what they saw and did on a crime scene. This section must be written chronologically and tell the story of the processing. It is imperative that the CSI write detailed, factual, and organized Investigator Notes. The Notes section should be broken down into paragraphs and separated

by locations, if applicable. A good general breakdown of the Notes section is:

- Describe the scene. Always start scene descriptions in general and get more specific (see Figure 5.10).
- Describe any anomalies with the evidence. Depending on the scene, this section may be excluded (see Figure 5.11).
- Describe the decedent/victim. Include the transportation of the decedent/victim, if known and applicable (see Figure 5.12).
- Describe any additional processing done on the scene or in the laboratory (see Figure 5.13).
- State where all the evidence was submitted (see Figure 5.13).

Not all of these sections will be included in every scene. In some scenes, there will be multiples of these sections. This is the area of

The scene consisted of a single story, single family home in a residential neighborhood. The home had a screened in porch on the rear of the home. There was an outdoor couch, chair, and two end tables near a stone fire pit in the backyard.

The scene consisted of a one story home in a residential neighborhood. The home was a three bedroom two bath home with a full kitchen, dining area, living room, screened in back porch, and attached garage.

The scene consisted of a large vacant parking lot. There was a sign at the entrance that said "European Village". The vehicle was found in a parking space facing east. The vehicle was locked. A pair of glasses and a cane could be seen on the front, right passenger seat.

The scene consisted of a three-story family home in a residential neighborhood. There was a for sale sign in front of the home and the home was mostly empty and clean. There were a couple pieces of furniture in various rooms in the home. There were cleaning rags in the first floor kitchen sink and on a rack in the garage. There was a mop bucket with water and a mop in the garage. The lights were on in the garage.

Figure 5.10 Several examples of how to describe a crime scene in the report.

The front door of the location had faint marks of a possible shoe impression. There was extensive damage to the front door frame. Pieces of the door frame were on the floor in the living room. The faceplate for the door lock was found on the couch. There was a plugin air freshener directly behind the door that appeared to have been forcibly pushed into the wall causing damage to the drywall. Just above the air freshener at a height equal to the front door handle there was more damage to the drywall.

Suspected blood could be seen on the interior of the interior garage door and a washer and dryer that sat just inside the door. Suspected blood could be seen on the floor in this laundry room, the living room, dining room, and foyer. There was also suspected blood on a chandelier above the dining room table, on numerous windows in the dining room, and on the door on the south side of the dining room. The door on the north side of the dining room that led to a screened in porch had a substantial amount of suspected blood on the interior glass. The location of this suspected blood was measured 1' 00" east of the door frame and 4' 04" up from the floor.

Figure 5.11 Examples of "anomalies" on a crime scene. These can include damage or bloodstains.

The decedent was found south of the vehicle in a supine position. Both of the decedent's arms were bent at the elbows. The majority of the decedent's body was on a grassy knoll in the middle of the parking lot. The decedent was fully clothed in pants, shirt, shoes and socks.

The decedent was located in the living room area, lying in the supine position in the middle of the area rug. The decedent was dressed only in a pair of shorts. His legs were extended out and both of his hands were resting on his chest. His head was resting on a book. The decedent appeared to have been deceased for some time and was in an active state of bloat. Livor mortis was present throughout the posterior portion of the decedent's body.

The decedent could be seen under the elevator, down the shaft, and on the ground at the first floor. The decedent was lying in a supine position, both legs and arms bent, and eyes open. She was fully clothed in a long sleeve shirt with another shirt underneath, long pants, and shoes (no socks visible). Her shirt was raised slightly at the waist. Suspected blood was visible on the bottom of her left hand. A closer look at the left hand showed injury to the top of the hand. Suspected blood could be seen on the ground near the decedent's feet.

Figure 5.12 Examples of how to describe a decedent.

On Tuesday, Date of processing at approximately 1055 hours, CSI CSI Name began the processing of Items #515.5-.8 (what the items were) for latent fingerprints. CSI anyone who was present or assisted assisted the following day. Below is a summary of the processing methods and results:

	Description	Methods	Results
515.5	One (1) piece (, silver in color	CYANOACRYLATE / MAGNETIC POWDER / WETWOP	NLOV*
515.6	One (1) (silver in color	CYANOACRYLATE / MAGNETIC POWDER	NLOV*
515.7	Four (4) pieces , silver in color	CYANOACRYLATE / MAGNETIC POWDER / WETWOP	NEGATIVE
515.8	One (1) roll (, silver in color	CYANOACRYLATE / MAGNETIC POWDER / WETWOP	NEGATIVE

NLOV* - No Latents of Value

All items recovered were photographed, packaged, sealed, initialed, and submitted to the Evidence Unit at the name of agency where evidence is located

Figure 5.13 An example of additional processing in the laboratory. Charts or tables are an easy way to quickly state the processing and results.

the report that must flow chronologically and be detailed to explain what was done and where the CSI went at all times. Including dates, times, locations, and personnel present is imperative for future readers and court purposes. The CSI must include all technical details and maintain objectivity when describing and explaining the scenes and the work that was done.

Rules of Thumb

When a CSI writes their report, they want to ensure they are following the rules of thumb of being detailed, factual, and organized throughout the entire report.

Detailed

CSI reports should be detailed and include descriptions of the evidence they see and recover as well as the entire scene. Often the context of a scene provides insight into why certain items were processed and/or collected or why they were not. CSIs must remember when they write the details of the scene and evidence, they are not giving their opinion. Conclusory or opinion terms such as "dirty" or "nasty" should be avoided. A CSI should clearly explain what they are seeing and avoid inserting their personal conclusions from the description. This is the first portion of the Investigator's Notes section of the report mentioned previously.

SCENE DESCRIPTION EXAMPLE (SEE ADDITIONAL EXAMPLES IN FIGURE 5.10):

The living room was full of boxes around the perimeter and into the middle of the room leaving only a narrow path to walk. There were visible spider webs in the corners of the room and all of the furniture and items in the room were covered in a layer of dust. There was a trash can in the corner that was overflowing with trash and various insects could be seen throughout the house.

In the above example, the reader begins to envision each component of the room based on the details provided. The CSI did not give their opinion or say the house was a "hoarder's" house or that the house was "filthy". The reader will draw their own conclusion of the location based on the details described. The photos will also show what the report is describing and lay out the crime scene for police officers, attorneys, and ultimately the jury.

Details should be included when describing the evidence as well. The CSI is the individual responsible for physical evidence and their photos and descriptions must accurately match what was collected. When describing evidence, CSIs should be as detailed as possible. They should always include the make, model, and serial number of any items they collect. These details are not only important in the specific case and scene where they are found but might also relate these items to other crimes or scenes. For example, a weapon with a serial number recovered at a shooting might be a weapon that was stolen during a prior burglary. This correlation can only be achieved by running a serial number through criminal justice databases; therefore, it is imperative to include this detail when describing the evidence. Details such as alterations should also be included. If, for example, a handgun is recovered and the serial number is obliterated or completely scratched off, this should be included in the description. Not only is serial number alteration an additional crime, but this alteration also makes the weapon unique and identifiable. Other details such as the color or any defects observed on an item should also be included when describing them in a report. Details of the scene and evidence help the reader to understand exactly what a CSI saw and recovered.

Factual

Writing factually can be very difficult for many CSIs. Factual means the CSI knows this to be true because they personally saw it or did it – observations without interpretation or reaction. When a CSI responds to a scene, they will be told a lot of information from a variety of individuals. All of that information is important and, as previously mentioned, should be included in the field notes. But when a CSI writes their final report, they should only report what they know to be true because they saw it or did it. For example, a CSI responds to a scene and the detective reports the decedent shot himself in his bedroom and is found on his side of the bed. This information is coming from the detective's investigation up to this point. Based on the testimonial evidence the detective is drawing conclusions: the decedent shot himself and the side of the bed belongs to the decedent. These are not "facts" to the CSI, these are hypotheses, and the CSI must try to prove or disprove them based on the physical evidence. Regardless of what the CSI finds and what they *believe* to be true, they must report only the facts. Continuing with the scenario, the CSI views the scene and observes a handgun on the decedent's right side and a wallet with an identification card that has a picture that matches the appearance of the decedent. When writing the report, the CSI should not state:

> The decedent shot himself and his identification was found on the nightstand next to him.

The CSI does not know the above statements to be true, therefore this is not factual. The CSI should write these details in the report but state them as facts:

> Item #01 (handgun) was recovered on the decedent's right side. A wallet with an identification card with the name 'John Smith' was found on the nightstand east of the decedent.

By writing the details in this manner the CSI is documenting and describing exactly what they saw, which is factual. This is often very challenging for CSIs who want to tell a reader what to think. The goal in writing factually is to document fact-based observations that will then be considered by individuals involved in the case along with information related to the crime derived from other sources.

Organized

A CSI report is a story and should be told in chronological order. CSIs cannot tell the story of what they did in the lab processing evidence if they never explained that they responded to the scene and collected that evidence. It is very important to keep field notes in chronological order as well to assist with the organization of the report. The report should always begin with when and how the CSI was notified of the case. This can occur in a variety of ways, a radio dispatch, in person, a cell phone call, but no matter how the CSI is notified it is very important they clearly state how they were told of the case. They must also indicate who contacted them and when. All of these details become very important in court and must be accurate.

Once the CSI explains how they were notified, they should discuss their arrival on the scene. Once arriving at the scene, the CSI will meet with officers, detectives, or other CSIs. They should explain who they met with and what information was relayed to them. After this portion of the report, CSIs should only discuss what they themselves did on the scene or in the lab. The order in which they write the report should always be chronological and if more than one scene was involved, they should indicate when they went to the new location.

Summary

As previously mentioned, specific report requirements will differ from agency to agency. It is important for CSIs to understand that by learning to write detailed, factual, organized reports, they will always do well in court. The templates and examples in this text are meant as guidance of a format that has worked for agencies in various locations throughout the country. Always adapt to the agency policy. As a CSI gains experience, they will create an organization to their report that works for them when testifying and meets the agency requirements. Report writing, similar to field notes, is very personal, and each CSI will develop their own style throughout the career. It is important for the CSI to learn a style that will keep their reports detailed, factual, and organized, and explain all of the scientific work the CSI did on the case.

End of Chapter Questions

1. What report components should be included in a CSI crime scene investigative report?
2. When would a CSI need to include hearsay in their report?
3. Why is weather an important element to include in a CSI report?
4. Give an example of items of evidence that a CSI submits to the Evidence Unit that might not have a photo placard number. Why would these items not have photo placard numbers?
5. What are the rules of thumb for CSI report writing?
6. What does it mean to write a report "chronologically"?
7. What is a factual description?

6

CSI Reports for Crime Scenes Involving Property Crimes

LAURA PAZARENA

Property Crimes

Property crimes are defined as crimes dealing with the theft or damage of property. Examples include, but are not limited to, commercial and residential burglaries and recovered stolen vehicles. When dealing with vehicles, CSIs must remember the vehicle is the crime scene, therefore they must describe the vehicle like they would a crime scene. Property crimes often include damage to the property and the CSI must clearly explain this in the report. It is important for the CSI to talk to the first responding officer(s) on the scene during their walk-through and understand what the normal condition of the property is. It is becoming increasingly more common for the initial report to be made online or over the telephone prior to the CSI's response. In this case, the CSI must conduct a walk-through with the complainant to determine what might have been taken or disturbed by the perpetrator(s). If, for example, a house has had a broken window for months that the homeowners have not had time to repair, this is not related to the crime and that should be clearly explained. The CSI should still mention the damage to keep the report factual, but in their overview and discussion of the walk-through, they should indicate that this damage was pre-existing. The type of information included in the report will depend on the type of crime and the amount of processing done on the scene or evidence collected.

DOI: 10.4324/9780429343162-8

Burglaries

Burglaries involve entering a location with the intent to commit another crime. Generally, CSIs are involved with burglaries of homes or businesses. When dealing with burglaries, or any damage or destruction of property, CSIs should be aware of, and thoroughly document, the conditions of the scene. ***Conditions of the scene*** refer to the cleanliness, level of disarray, forced entry, or any other descriptors that describe or help illustrate what the scene looked like. The conditions of the scene will help the reader understand the amount of disturbance that took place in the house. As mentioned previously, it is imperative that the CSI talk to the investigating officer(s) and/or complainant(s) and gain an understanding of the "normal" conditions of the scene so that they can fully understand if the conditions they are seeing are relevant to the crime. The condition of the house will often guide the processing for a CSI on these scenes. CSIs want to focus on areas that were disturbed by the suspect(s); therefore obtaining a thorough understanding of the conditions is imperative (see Figure 6.1).

In addition to the conditions of the scene, the CSI should describe the ***characteristics of the scene***. The characteristics include the layout, general floor plan, and description of the location. This is important for all reports, but in burglary cases, this helps identify the access points to the location, which can be critical in these cases. Floorplans help explain alternative entrances and exits as well as the accessibility to areas that the suspect(s) focused on when they came in. A factual, thorough description of the location will help readers understand exactly what may have taken place.

Investigator's Notes:

The scene consisted of a single story family home in a residential neighborhood. All the windows, except for one on the back side of the residence were boarded up with plywood. The foyer area and kitchen were cluttered with boxes, mail, medications and other various household items. The master bedroom, in the northeast corner of the residence, also appeared cluttered with clothing and multiple watches and watch boxes. The bedroom in the north corner of the residence was extremely cluttered and appeared to be a makeshift gunsmith workshop. There were multiple firearms, cartridges, cartridge casings, gun powders, and other ammunition making supplies. The living room area also appeared in a bit of disarray. The coffee table appeared to have been knocked crooked and the area rug appeared bunched up under one of the legs to the coffee table. A fan was knocked over and a reclining chair appears turned around. There were multiple extension cords stretched around the living room area on the floor. Magazines and books were also strewn around on the floor.

Figure 6.1 Example of conditions of the scene.

Recovered Stolen Property/Vehicles

CSIs are often involved in the processing of recovered stolen property. When the property is recovered law enforcement wants to forensically link a suspect to the property. Oftentimes this is done through fingerprint processing and collection of swabs for DNA testing. CSIs get involved in these cases in a variety of ways. CSIs may assist with search warrants at suspects' houses or may respond to the scene of a recovered stolen vehicle. Regardless of how the CSI gets involved, these cases often involve processing a variety of items that may not normally be considered "evidence". Recovered stolen vehicles quite frequently have items left behind by suspects such as cigarette butts, candy wrappers, drink containers, receipts, or other trash and these items are excellent items to process for fingerprints and/or swab for the possible presence of DNA (see Figure 6.2).

Walgreens
6.2a: Iodine fuming of a receipt.
6.2b: Fingerprints recovered from a candy wrapper.

Figure 6.2 Fingerprint processing of items traditionally thought of as "trash".

Processing recovered stolen property is the time when CSIs most often "think like suspects" and process any and everything they think the suspect handled. For these types of cases, it is also important for the CSI to remember that the vehicle is the crime scene and must be thoroughly described in the report. Important details such as the amount of damage to the vehicle, license plate number, state (or other issuing authority), vehicle identification number, the position of the seats, if there is a key in the ignition if the ignition has been damaged, and the items found in the car are critical in these cases (see Figure 6.3).

Another important consideration is the search method for vehicles. Vehicles should be searched using the zone method. A ***Zone Search*** involves dividing the area to be searched into adjacent zones. The smaller the size of the zone, the more methodical the search can be. This searching method is used for confined spaces like vehicles, or for vast areas that need to be broken down, such as acreage of land. When searching and processing vehicles the CSI should break the vehicle down into zones and methodically search and process each area. The report should clearly indicate how the vehicle was broken down into zones and specifically where items of evidence were recovered or where processing was done within each zone. The way the CSI labels the zones is their decision, as long as they can explain their methodology to others during the investigation and during the trial (see Figure 6.4).

It is important for a CSI to clearly indicate where each zone is located. Vehicle zones are one of the few times a CSI can use directionals such as "right" and "left" or "driver's side" and "passenger side" as long as they can clearly explain when testifying the viewpoint

Investigator's Notes:

The vehicle was located in the secure Forensic Unit Garage at the agency name Center. All doors and windows were secure with red evidence tape. The doors were unlocked and there were no keys recovered with the vehicle. The rear tires were missing off the vehicle and the rear suspension of the vehicle was resting on a set of tires. There were several minor dents and scrapes on the exterior of the vehicle. There was no noticeable damage to the interior of the vehicle. The front driver's side window was partially open and there was blue tape covering the gap from the interior. The glovebox was open and there was blue tape attached to the glovebox and dash board. Detective conducted a search of the vehicle and turned over Items #515.1-1-7 (miscellaneous items), #515.3 (tray), and #515.4 (sock) to CSI on scene. Detective later made contact with the victim who advised she did not have tape on the window or the glovebox. Detective then requested the tape be removed for evidence processing. Item #515.1-8-9 (rolls of tape) and Item #515.2 (tape) were recovered by CSI .

Figure 6.3 Example of the beginning stages of processing a recovered stolen vehicle.

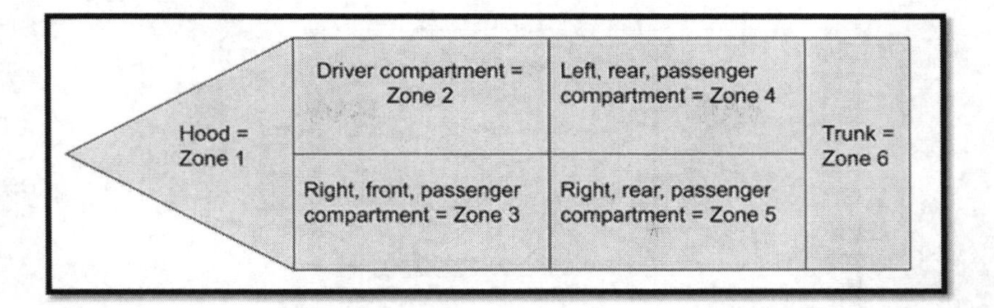

Figure 6.4 Zone breakdown of a vehicle.

of these positions. In Figure 6.4, "right" and "left" are from the viewpoint of being inside of the vehicle. If an individual is outside of the vehicle, standing at the hood, facing the car, right and left are opposite. The CSI should understand what viewpoint they are using and be able to clearly explain it in court. When processing this vehicle for fingerprints or collecting samples for DNA testing, it is crucial the CSI clearly labels the fingerprint cards and swabs with the exact location of recovery. Many agencies have pre-printed fingerprint cards that make this an easy process (see Figure 6.5a). The CSI wants to ensure their report exactly matches the wording they write on the fingerprint cards or swab boxes being submitted (see Figure 6.5b). If the fingerprint cards or swabs collected by the CSI are sent for comparison, the results will come back referencing the labeling on the cards or packaging (see Figure 6.5c). If the CSI does not ensure the wording matches on every item and the report, the results may be difficult to tie back to any specific portion of the vehicle, making the evidence difficult to present in court (see Figure 6.5).

When writing a report involving recovered stolen property details such as the make, model, and serial number of the items is critical. This will help investigators and evidence custodians locate the rightful owners of the property. In addition, these details may provide important evidence establishing that a crime was committed. For example, if a CSI locates a fingerprint on a piece of property that can be linked by serial number to an owner who reported the item missing and that fingerprint is later linked to a suspect, that fingerprint would likely be important evidence in a criminal case against the suspect. Therefore this information is important for a CSI to annotate when they are listing their items of evidence in the report.

Automobile Backing Card (LP#01)

Case #

Address of Incident:

Prints lifted by:

Badge #

Type of crime: RECVD. ST. VEH.

Victim name:

Suspect name: UNK

Location of prints lifted: INT FRONT (R) PSSGR DOOR FRAME

Lift # 01

Year/Make: 2008/CHEVY

Model: SUBURBAN

Color: WHITE

Tag state #

VIN #

Circle Number Where Prints Found

FRONT 3 4 (5) 6 7 8 2 17 18 19 9 1 10 16 15 14 13 12 11

Front Windshield · Rear Window · Windows

6.5a: Pre-printed evidentiary fingerprint card submitted. Notice the wording for the "location of print lifted".

Item #619.4: One (1) manila envelope containing Latent Prints #01-02, labeled as follows:

LP #01: One (1) latent print card recovered from the interior, front, right passenger door frame
LP #02: One (1) latent print card recovered from the interior, front, right passenger door

6.5b: Fingerprint portion of the report. Notice that LP#01 matches the fingerprint card labeling exactly from 5.5a above without shorthand.

Re: ID#
Case#

The Latent Print Unit has identified a latent print on Item 1 of 2 labeled "Int Front R Pssgr Door Frame" which was submitted in reference to the above case. The print has been identified as the following individual:

Suspect Name DOB
FBI#

6/5c: Results from the fingerprint card in 5.5a being sent for comparison. Notice they referenced the wording from the fingerprint card exactly.

Figure 6.5 The CSI wants to ensure that the words they write in the report describing the location of the recovery of fingerprints match exactly what they wrote on the evidentiary cards. Notice in the results received, they quote the words on the card exactly as they were written. This can be tied back to the report and the CSI can easily testify to where these were recovered from and how they recovered them.

Summary

CSIs often get involved in the processing of evidence recovered from property crimes. The evidence in these cases is oftentimes not items the CSI would traditionally consider, such as candy wrappers, straws, or receipts. In property crime cases, however, these non-traditional items of evidence are often the most probative and should be processed fully. It is imperative that the CSI thoroughly photograph the evidence in these cases and document all identifying information in order to possibly return items to their rightful owners and link suspects to the crimes. Most importantly, the labeling on the fingerprint cards or swab boxes must exactly match the report so the CSI can easily testify to the recovery location and processing methods for each item.

End of Chapter Questions

1. What is a property crime?
2. What is burglary?
3. What is the difference between the characteristics of the scene and the conditions of the scene?
4. What is a zone search and what is it used for?
5. Why is the labeling of fingerprint cards and swab boxes so important?

Reference

Gardner, Ross M. *Practical Crime Scene Processing and Investigation*. Third ed., Boca Raton, FL, CRC Press, 2019.

7

CSI Reports for Crime Scenes Involving Crimes against a Person

LAURA PAZARENA

Persons Crimes

Persons crimes are crimes that are committed against people that involve direct physical harm or other abuse of a person. These include, but are not limited to, robbery, assault, sex crimes, and murder. These cases may be simple and straightforward, but often they become complicated and include multiple locations, people, and agencies. CSIs must ensure they follow the guidelines of report writing and note-taking and keep their information detailed, factual, and organized. CSIs and other criminal investigators are regularly exposed to the worst things humans do to each other. It is easy to have an emotional reaction to crimes committed against people, especially those dealing with the elderly and children. CSIs must remain neutral and not allow their emotional reactions to dictate how they report or process a scene. No matter how terrible the event is, CSIs must always remember to objectively report all of the facts. While this may be very challenging, it must remain the fundamental goal for the CSI report.

Death Investigations

Regardless of the medicolegal death investigation system in place in the jurisdiction, CSIs respond to most death cases within their jurisdiction. The main exception to this is death cases that involve a natural death. Most agencies do not send their investigative team to natural death calls. A ***natural death*** is a death due to natural disease. This includes, but is not limited to, atherosclerotic cardiovascular

DOI: 10.4324/9780429343162-9

disease, diabetes, hypertension, cancer, and dementia. Cases that involve an individual who dies from unnatural causes, or whose death appears suspicious, are generally investigated by detectives and CSIs. It is imperative for a CSI to remember the basic steps in crime scene processing and the scientific method when working these scenes. Something to remember is that the call and information the CSI receives initially will often change as the CSI processes the scene and works the investigation. Crime scenes have a tendency to tell a very different story from the original report and CSIs are responsible for telling that story. It is imperative that CSIs remain neutral when working scenes and not let the potentially biasing information of the initial report direct their investigation. If a case is initially reported as a suicide, the CSI must remember this is only the original hypothesis; they must examine the crime scene and find evidence to support or refute this hypothesis and then report the facts. At no point in time should a CSI definitively say a case is a homicide or a suicide in their report, they should always report the facts of the scene. The facts are what allows the medical examiner or coroner's office to determine the manner of death. The ***manner of death*** is defined as the means by which the individual died. There are generally five categories of the manner of death, depending on the medical or coroner's office. The categories of the manner of death are:

1. Natural
    a. These are deaths that involve natural diseases. Generally, death is expected, or something suddenly exacerbates a natural condition, for example, an asthma attack. Asthma is a natural disease, if someone has a sudden asthma attack and is unable to get help soon enough, this may be a sudden unexpected death, but it is still considered natural.
2. Homicide
    a. These are deaths in which an individual is killed by another person. When medical examiners and coroners designate homicide as the manner of death, they are not looking into the intent; they are simply stating if the decedent died at the hands of another person. The intent is determined by the investigation done by law enforcement, often this includes evidence collected by CSIs.

3. Suicide
   a. These are deaths in which an individual intentionally kills themselves. In order for a medical examiner or coroner to state a death is a suicide, they generally require information about the scene and the investigation. Crime scene photographs from the CSI are almost always used in these cases. Photos of any suicide notes, signs of planning, and the exact location of weapons or ligatures on the scene are imperative in these cases.
4. Accident
   a. These are unintentional deaths. These cases often include drug overdose cases, motor vehicle collisions, and accidental falls.
5. Undetermined
   a. The law enforcement investigation is imperative for a medical examiner or coroner to determine the manner of death. In some cases, such as drownings, it may be difficult to determine the true manner of death. If a decedent is found floating in a lake, the question is did they walk into the water on purpose which would be a suicide, were they pushed in by someone, which would be a homicide, or did they fall in, which would be an accident. The autopsy will only be able to determine the cause of death, but the manner of death may be classified as undetermined by the coroner or medical examiner. It is important to note that a death that is classified as "undetermined" may still result in criminal prosecution and, therefore, the CSI's processing of the scene and evidence and reporting procedures should be conducted in accordance with the practices previously discussed.

CSIs play an integral part in the investigation and the determination of the manner of death. Depending on the policies and practices of the CSI's jurisdiction, CSIs should attend autopsies when possible, to provide their photos and input of the crime scene to the medical examiner or coroner. When writing death reports, CSIs should include that they attended the autopsy and any preliminary results that they learned at the autopsy. CSIs will be able to obtain information about the exact number of wounds on a body and the trajectory or path projectiles or sharp instruments taken inside of the body. This section of the Investigator Notes is the only other time, besides the Overview, that a CSI will write hearsay. The CSI should indicate the date, time, location, and who was with them at autopsy and any results that they were told in the Investigator Notes section of their report. It is important that this is chronological in the report. These preliminary findings relayed from the forensic pathology team during an autopsy will help inform and guide the investigation while awaiting the final autopsy report which often can take months to complete (see Figure 7.1).

When writing death investigation reports, a thorough description of the decedent should be included. An important note, victims of death investigations are referred to as ***decedents*** which means they are deceased. Living victims are not decedents and should be referred to as victims. When describing people, a CSI must remember to write factually. When they observe someone on the scene, they want to objectively state how the person *appears* to them. Descriptions should be written as:

> The decedent appeared to be a white female, with blonde hair, wearing blue jeans, a yellow t-shirt, shoes, and socks.

CSIs do not want to state that the decedent *is a white female.* CSIs will be surprised to discover at autopsy that what they originally thought on the scene may not be accurate; therefore they should always state how individuals appeared to them to keep the reports factual. This is especially true when dealing with decedents that are in various stages of decomposition. The longer an individual is deceased, the more decomposed and unidentifiable they become. CSIs do not want to

Tuesday, – *Office of the Medical Examiner*

On date of autopsy attendance at approximately 1000 hours CSI and Detective attended the autopsy of the decedent. Dr. stated that the decedent had an entrance wound to the right temple above the hairline that measured 1/16" in diameter. The shot was from right to left and Item #619.3 (projectile) was recovered from the occipital lobe of the brain. This item was turned over to CSI

Figure 7.1 A good way to list autopsy findings is to create a new paragraph stating the date, location, who was present, what was found, and any evidence recovered.

claim that someone is "visually identifiable" or a "white female" when they look like as shown in Photo 7.1.

This individual is obviously not identifiable, and if the CSI writes in the report gender, race, or age for this person, their inaccurate observation could be used as a point of impeachment in court. CSIs should state the facts only about the decedent, if the CSI is not comfortable stating a race, gender, or age they should not list one in the report. CSIs must remember that they need to be able to explain and testify to everything they write in the report. They should be confident in their writing and their ability to support what they stated in their report and why.

Another important detail about describing decedents is their clothing and any injuries. Important details about clothing include, but are not limited to, if items such as pants or underwear are pulled down or if belts and zippers are undone. Tears or rips in clothing or any defects from possible weapons should also be indicated. The defects or exact positioning of clothing can impact the investigation; therefore CSIs must thoroughly document these. Oftentimes, CSIs are responsible for collecting the decedent's clothing from the autopsy. CSIs should take these items back to the lab, lay them out, and thoroughly document them through photography. The report should clearly indicate the make, model, and size (if applicable) of each item (see Figure 7.2) as well as the exact locations and sizes of any defects.

Defects in clothing are something that would be considered an *anomaly* and would be discussed in the lab processing section of the

Photo 7.1 This decedent is not visually identifiable.

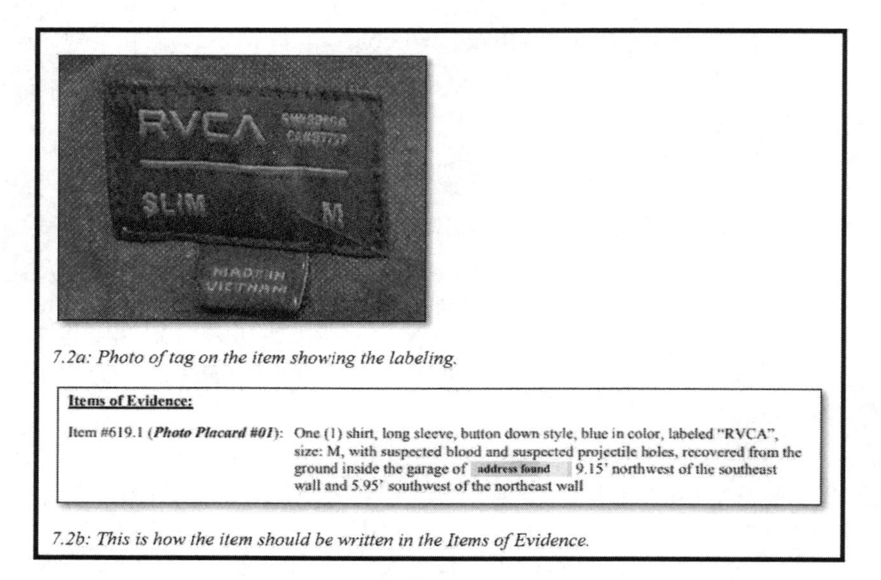

7.2a: Photo of tag on the item showing the labeling.

Items of Evidence:

Item #619.1 (***Photo Placard #01***): One (1) shirt, long sleeve, button down style, blue in color, labeled "RVCA", size: M, with suspected blood and suspected projectile holes, recovered from the ground inside the garage of address found 9.15' northwest of the southeast wall and 5.95' southwest of the northeast wall

7.2b: This is how the item should be written in the Items of Evidence.

Figure 7.2 The tag of a shirt and the associated description in the report. Notice that the description includes the make and size, which matches the photo (7.2a) exactly. It also mentions that there are defects in the shirt, which will be discussed in the Investigator's Notes.

Investigator's Notes. These defects should be labeled by the CSI and their location should be clearly explained in the report. A defect on the front of a shirt versus the back of a shirt could be significant to the investigation; therefore completing detailed photography and written descriptions is imperative. The details of the make, model, and size (if applicable) would be listed in the Items of Evidence section. Refer to Chapter 4 for details on how to list items of evidence (see Figure 7.3).

Injuries should be described as what they appeared to be. Similar to decedents, the CSI does not know with certainty that an injury is a gunshot or a stab wound. They should list injuries as they appear to them, stating something like, "there appeared to be a gunshot wound on the right temple and another wound on the left temple". CSIs should not state in their reports if injuries are entry or exit but should include their exact location and the quantity. While on the scene, CSIs should always discuss their hypotheses and opinions of the wounds they are seeing with the detectives. CSIs should have knowledge of the various types of gunshot wounds and should look for evidence to support their opinion. Photography of all wounds with and without rulers should be done and the photos should be clear and close enough

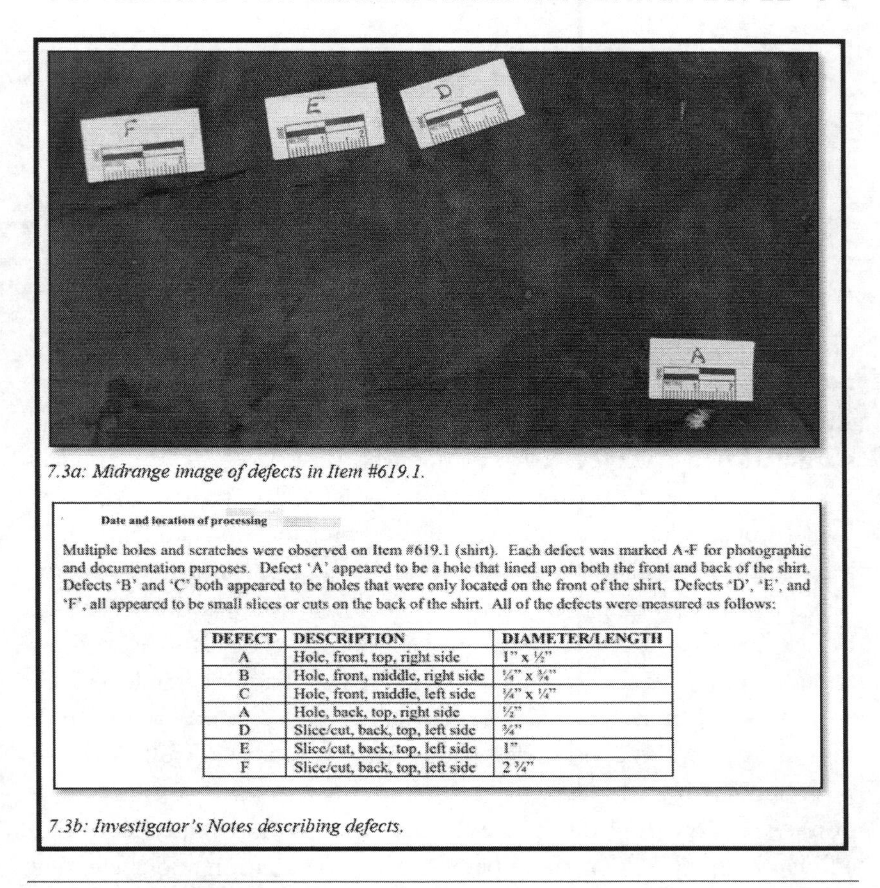

7.3a: Midrange image of defects in Item #619.1.

Date and location of processing

Multiple holes and scratches were observed on Item #619.1 (shirt). Each defect was marked A-F for photographic and documentation purposes. Defect 'A' appeared to be a hole that lined up on both the front and back of the shirt. Defects 'B' and 'C' both appeared to be holes that were only located on the front of the shirt. Defects 'D', 'E', and 'F', all appeared to be small slices or cuts on the back of the shirt. All of the defects were measured as follows:

DEFECT	DESCRIPTION	DIAMETER/LENGTH
A	Hole, front, top, right side	1" x ½"
B	Hole, front, middle, right side	¼" x ¾"
C	Hole, front, middle, left side	¼" x ¼"
A	Hole, back, top, right side	½"
D	Slice/cut, back, top, left side	¾"
E	Slice/cut, back, top, left side	1"
F	Slice/cut, back, top, left side	2 ¾"

7.3b: Investigator's Notes describing defects.

Figure 7.3 Defects in Item #619.1 and associated description in report. Tables are a succinct way to get measurements into a report.

to see details such as stippling or soot. When photographing wounds, always remember the rules of photography and include overall, mid-range, and close-up photos to show the exact locations of the injuries. These photos will support the opinions discussed on the scene, but those opinions should never be written in the report. Unless a CSI is qualified based on their background, training, and experience to testify as an expert to the distances of gunshot wounds, their opinion should not be in the report. The report should remain factual and state only the location and description of the injuries. The photos will show the injuries and if needed, the attorneys on the case can get experts to testify to the distances of the shots. Injuries from various weapons may appear different on the body and CSIs should be cautious about

The decedent was found in a prone position in the hallway on the east side of the house. He was fully clothed in pants, t-shirt, socks, and slippers. There was visible suspected blood underneath the decedent's left arm. There was suspected bruising to the decedent's left hand and a white in color bracelet on his left forearm. Suspected blood could be seen on the decedent's left index finger.

Items #619.3-.5 (knives) were found in varying positions around the decedent's body. Item #619.6 (shotgun) was found with the butt of the gun propped against the west wall of the hallway and the firearms cabinet. The muzzle of the gun was facing east at the feet of the decedent.

Ms. [redacted] from the Office of the Medical Examiner (OME) responded to the scene. Upon moving the decedent a large hole could be seen in the epigastric area. The hole had suspected burning around the edges. The bracelet on the decedent's left arm was observed to be a hospital bracelet. Ms. [redacted] had the decedent transported to her office.

Figure 7.4 This description of the decedent indicates the observations made by the CSI on the scene but never states any specific types of injuries. This type of description keeps the report factual.

stating the injury type. Always describe how wounds and injuries appear. Some exit gunshot wounds may look like stab wounds and a CSI does not want to include an incorrect personal conclusion in a factual report. It is imperative that the CSI list and describe any and all wounds or injuries that they observe while on the scene (see Figure 7.4). As discussed previously, the CSI will also discuss any and all wounds observed during the autopsy. At autopsy, injuries may be numbered or lettered and explained. If this is done, the injuries should be photographed and explained in the report as well.

When writing death investigation reports, the crime scene description is also very important. The details of the crime scene description will vary depending on the type of death investigation and the extent of the scene. As with all cases, the CSI should start with a general scene description and then get more specific.

Robberies/Assaults/Sex Crimes

Persons crimes that do not involve a death investigation will have living victims. ***Victims*** are individuals who are still alive and have suffered injury or loss from the event. When CSIs are involved in cases with victims, they should be aware of the emotional state of these individuals and always ask permission to photograph them, touch them, and collect evidence from them. CSIs have a legal authority to investigate crimes involving victims, but they must be aware of the individual's rights and always know what they are allowed to do on a scene. An important note for CSIs is an individual's right to privacy in their home and property. If a CSI gets called to an event that is inside someone's home or vehicle, the CSI must ensure they have the proper legal documentation to process the scene. This generally means law enforcement has obtained either a warrant for the location or consent to search the property. Anything a CSI does, including processing, is a form of search and cannot be done without the proper legal documentation.

Robbery is the taking of property from within the direct vicinity of the victim. Oftentimes, robbery is committed with force and a victim may be threatened with a weapon or injured during the crime. ***Assaults*** are physical attacks of a victim. Assaults vary in their severity, but any unwanted contact with a victim constitutes an assault. CSIs generally get involved in more serious assault cases. Many times, victims of robberies are also assaulted during the crime. Depending on the severity of the assault, the victim may be transported to the hospital. It is important for the CSI to ascertain the location of the victim immediately upon arrival on the scene. If they are able to photograph and document the victim prior to being transported, they should do this to obtain images of the injuries before being cleaned or stitched. If the CSI does not see the victim on scene and they are at the hospital, the CSI will need to go to the hospital to document any injuries and collect any evidence such as clothing, if needed. For these cases, thorough documentation of the victim's injuries, as well as any defensive wounds, their hands, and their clothing, are imperative. ***Defensive wounds*** are any injuries that may have been caused while the victim was trying to defend themselves against the assailant. Often CSIs will find defensive wounds along the forearms or hands when they are handling robbery and assault cases. The victim will frequently put their arms up to block their face or body and get injured on the forearms or hands. These are very important to document, as these injuries may support the testimonial evidence of the victim or witnesses.

Sex crimes involve unwanted sexual conduct or contact and can include acts of sexual abuse, sexual assault, or rape. These are particularly sensitive cases for the victims and the family of the victims. The processing of these scenes often involves taking clothing and bedding and a CSI should always be able to thoroughly explain to the victim and family why they are taking the items they are recovering. Crime scenes related to sex crimes often involve the search for possible DNA evidence. The sequence of processing for these scenes is important as well as limiting contamination. ***Contamination*** is the introduction of foreign material to an object or scene. As soon as a CSI steps foot into a crime scene they minimally contaminate the scene. The dirt on the bottom of their boots falls onto the floor and introduces contamination. This is why proper personal protective equipment (PPE) is required. ***Personal protective equipment (PPE)*** are tools used to protect the CSI from contaminants. Items such as gloves and booties are examples of PPE and should always be worn by a CSI on the scene to limit the amount of contamination they cause on a scene. When processing sex crime scenes, CSIs may also want to consider hair nets, tyvex suits, and face masks. These scenes often involve looking for the suspect's hair on the bed or on the victim as well as vaginal or seminal fluid in the scene. To find biological specimens, such as vaginal or seminal fluid, CSIs generally use alternate light sources (ALS). An ***ALS*** is a light that gives off different wavelengths and assists in identifying a variety of forms of evidence. ALS is often used for the discovery of biological fluids such as blood, semen, saliva, urine, and vaginal fluid. ALS can also be used when processing with fluorescent powders or when looking for gunshot residue. When using an ALS on a crime scene related to a sex crime, the CSI must ensure they are using the correct nanometer of light. If an ALS is used on the scene, the CSI must ensure they document the nanometer they are utilizing for their report. When writing the investigative report, the CSI must ensure they are explaining thoroughly the on-scene processing. After describing the scene, the CSI should explain their use of the ALS, state what nanometer of light and barrier filter they used, and the results. To ensure that the ALS is working properly a positive and negative *control* should be examined prior to analyzing the scene. A ***control*** is a material of known composition that is analyzed to evaluate the performance of a test to demonstrate that the method or equipment works correctly, and the results are valid. Positive controls confirm that the procedure will produce the expected result. Negative controls confirm that the procedure does not produce an unintended result. The successful completion of the controls should be documented in the notes and final report.

If the ALS reveals any possible fluids, the CSI should collect samples. This must also be indicated in the report and the samples will be listed as items of evidence. Depending on the item the fluid is found on, the CSI can collect samples in a variety of ways. If the fluid is on a large item such as a mattress, the CSI can do a cutting, a swab, or collect the entire mattress. A ***cutting*** is when a CSI cuts out an area of the larger item to submit as an item of evidence. If the item is a mattress, the CSI would cut out the area that the ALS showed fluid. This entire cutting can be submitted to the lab for testing. The CSI could also swab the area or collect the entire mattress. Something for CSIs to consider when making the decision of which collection method is best is the revictimization of the victim. The CSI does not want the victim to have to go through any more trauma; therefore if taking the entire mattress would cause the victim more stress or trauma, the CSI may want to consider one of the other alternatives. The CSI, however, must do what is best for the case, and choose the most probative collection method based on the particular facts of the case. Any small items that a CSI recovers, such as hairs, should be thoroughly documented as well and placed in a pharmacist fold. ***Pharmacist folds*** are small envelopes that the CSI can create on the scene from any piece of paper (Figure 7.5).

Pharmacist folds are convenient for any scene and should be used whenever trace evidence is recovered. When writing these items in the investigative report, the CSI is listing the item of evidence, not the fold – it is simply the packaging. They should include the specific location the item was found. In sex crime cases, for example, hairs found under the comforter, on the fitted sheet, in the center of the bed could have huge impacts on the case. Whereas, hairs found on the pillowcase may not be as probative. The specific location of recovery may be very important and should always be listed in the report with the item of evidence.

Summary

Persons crimes are very personal not only for the people involved but for the CSI as well. A CSI must take care when working on these cases to not let their emotions get involved in the case and remain objective during their investigation. All information must be reported factually, and the CSI must properly explain the scene and the injuries they observe. Oftentimes, injuries and defects in these cases become

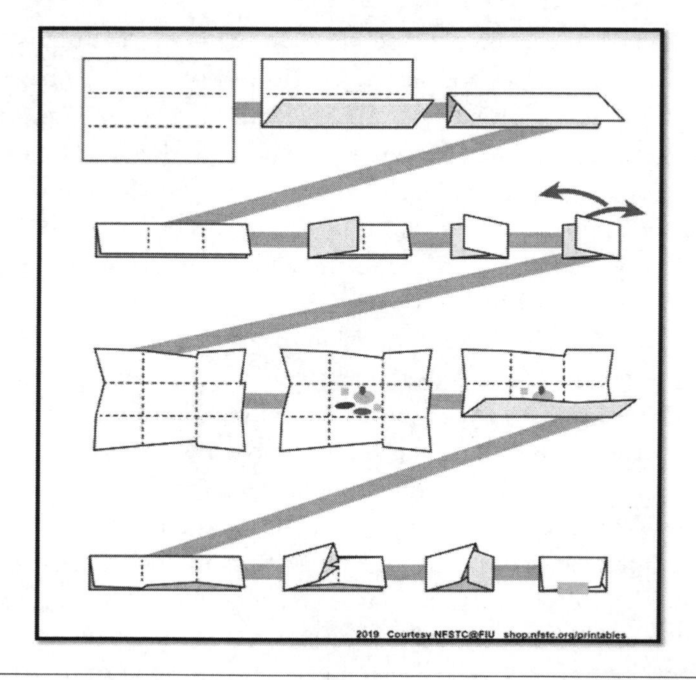

2019 Courtesy NFSTC@FIU shop.nfstc.org/printables

Figure 7.5 Example of how to create a pharmacist fold courtesy of Florida International University.

very important and it is crucial CSIs report the details factually and accurately.

End of Chapter Questions

1. State, define, and give an example of each of the manners of death.
2. Which manner of death do CSIs not get involved in very often? Why?
3. What is the difference between a decedent and a victim?
4. What are defects in clothing and why are they important?
5. Why is PPE important for a CSI?
6. What is a control?
7. What is a pharmacist fold used for?

SECTION 3

Processing Report Writing

8

General Guidelines for Writing Reports for Cases That CSIs Processed in the Lab

LAURA PAZARENA

Introduction

CSIs should document everything they do for a case, no matter how minimal their involvement. Oftentimes, CSIs are asked to photograph items and nothing more. Photographing is a form of processing, and any involvement a CSI has should always be documented in a report. CSIs do not respond to all crimes in their jurisdiction. Many times, officers or detectives will process scenes and collect evidence, and a CSI may never get involved in the scene investigation. Depending on these cases and the investigation, CSIs may be asked to process the evidence recovered by other members of their agency in the lab for fingerprints or the collection of possible DNA. When this happens, the CSI needs to write a report, but this report will differ from a scene report since the CSI never responded to the scene. The fundamental grammar and punctuation rules will always apply and many of the guidelines for the investigative report will apply, but there are some variations that will be discussed in this chapter. A ***Processing Report*** is the report written for the cases when the CSI does not respond to the crime scene but rather analyzes or processes the evidence in the lab or at their agency.

Report Components

The Processing Report should be written chronologically and should begin with how the CSI was notified that their assistance is needed and should end with the CSI's last involvement in the case, generally

DOI: 10.4324/9780429343162-11

the submission of the evidence to the evidence and property unit. The general components for these reports are similar to the investigative report, with some variations:

- Case Information
    - Every report should include the case information. The case information should be from the original event. This information should include the case number, the address of the original crime scene, the date and time of processing, the CSI's name and identification number, the type of case, and the names of the people involved if known. It is important to note that the date of the offense and the date of processing for these cases are generally not the same. The offense and the original collection of evidence usually happened by someone else, and it is important that the CSI fill these dates and times appropriately. The author has found that having this information in a table at the top of the report is the easiest way for the CSI and readers of the report to reference the material (see Figure 8.1).
- Case Overview
    - The report should begin with a chronological overview of the case. The first portion should begin with the notification, how did the CSI get involved in this case? The CSI should clearly indicate when they were notified, how they were notified, and by whom they were notified. For these types of cases, the CSI is generally notified in person or through a written request. Depending on the agency, these requests may be via email or through an agency system. The CSI needs to clearly explain how and when they were notified. Unlike investigative reports, there is generally no scene response; therefore the case overview should summarize what the request said and clearly articulate what is being asked of the CSI (see Figure 8.2).

<table>
<tr><td>CASE NUMBER:</td><td>CSI:</td><td>DATE (of offense):</td><td>DATE (of processing):</td><td>APPROX. TIME (of processing):</td></tr>
<tr><td colspan="2">COMPLAINANT, VICTIM, WITNESS, DECEDENT, SUSPECT:</td><td colspan="3">OFFENSE:</td></tr>
<tr><td colspan="5">LOCATION OF OFFENSE:</td></tr>
</table>

Figure 8.1 An example of a case information box.

Case Overview:

On DATE REQUEST WAS RECEIVED at approximately 1403 hours, the Forensic Unit received a processing request, via HOW RECEIVED from Detective requesting assistance processing a recovered stolen item. Detective made contact with Crime Scene Investigator (CSI) in person, and advised that a laptop was recovered from the above listed location and was later determined to have been stolen during a vehicle burglary in . Detective made contact with a detective with Police Department who requested the laptop be processed for latent prints. CSI retrieved the item from the Evidence Unit at the Sheriff's Office. The following services were provided:

Figure 8.2 An example of the case overview for a processing report.

- Weather
  - Weather for these cases will depend on the type of case and the agency storage. Most frequently weather is listed when the CSI is asked to process vehicles that have been recovered and are being stored in an outdoor secure facility. In most processing cases, the weather is not relevant since the work is being done indoors.
- Vehicle
  - The vehicle section for these reports will only be needed if the evidence being processed is a vehicle. What is important to note is the CSI must list the vehicle item number *exactly* as it is labeled on the evidentiary vehicle and the chain of custody (COC). The vehicle being processed in these cases was recovered by someone else and should already be labeled with an item number. This is the item number the CSI should list in their report. This provides consistency and clarity when testifying.
- Digital Images/Video
  - These sections are the same as for an investigative report. The CSI should include the total number of images taken, what they are of, who took them, and where they can be found.
- Items of Evidence Processed
  - This section should be listed like the Items of Evidence section in an investigative report. In this section, the CSI is listing the items that they are taking out of the Evidence Unit. All items have already been collected and submitted by someone else; therefore the CSI needs to go to the Evidence Unit and retrieve them. When they retrieve the items, they should list the item number and what the

item is with all of the detail that they would include in an investigative report. There are some variations to what is included since these items were not recovered by the CSI on scene. For these items the CSI should include:

- Item number – Every single item should be given a unique item number and should already be labeled with a number. Make sure to write the item number exactly as it appears on the packaging for the item.
- Quantity – This should be the number of items in the envelope or package. When the CSI opens the package, they want to make sure they annotate exactly how many "things" are inside.
- What the item is – The proper names and terms for items must be used at all times. No matter how the package is labeled, the CSI wants to use the correct terms in their report. The CSI is not making any changes to the packaging, so the exterior labels will remain the same, but their report should be accurate and state what the item is using the correct terms. If the correct term is different from the package, the CSI must be prepared to explain their nomenclature in court.
- Color of the item – A general color should be included when describing items. CSIs want to make sure they are listing the colors factually. Similar to what the item is, the color may not match the packaging. The CSI must be prepared to explain why they wrote the color the way they did. Color is always "appeared to be" or "____in color" to keep the descriptions factual and remove any liability from the CSI.
- Labels/identifying features – Most items have some labeling or markings on them, and a CSI should indicate them if they are observed. Some items, such as projectiles, may have no labelings. If items have no labels, the CSI may exclude this portion of the description. Whenever possible, CSIs want to include at least the make, model, and serial number of items they recover. This is critical for items such as firearms that could be linked to several crimes or to the owner by serial number. CSIs do not need to list out every

single word written on an item, but they do want to include the basics that will help investigators and evidence custodians locate owners.

- Items of Evidence Recovered
  - This section is for any new items of evidence that the CSI recovers. If a CSI is processing a vehicle and they recover one handgun from under the driver's seat, three fingerprints, and collect three swabs, the handgun would be listed in this section and the prints and swabs would be listed in those sections. Any new items will need to be written as they are in an investigative report (see Chapter 4 for details). The recovery location for these will generally not include measurements since the CSI did not go to a scene.
- Prints/Swabs
  - These sections will be for any new prints or swabs the CSI collects off of any item they process. These sections must be clearly written to explain what specific item they recovered the prints or swabs from. These items will get item numbers and be listed the same as they are in the investigative report.
- Investigator's Notes
  - This is the bulk of the report. In this section, the CSI must explain how the items of evidence were packaged and sealed when they retrieved them. This documentation serves to validate that the item(s) being processed by the CSI were securely stored and free of tampering at the time the CSI took possession. Unlike investigative reports, these reports do not have a scene description. The CSI will begin by explaining that they retrieved the items from the Evidence Unit and then must explain how they are packaged. This description should match the photos of the items and it is imperative to keep the chain of custody intact and show that no tampering has occurred with respect to the items. Any lab processing that was done should be thoroughly explained as well as the results of the processing including any controls performed. After processing, all items should be resealed, initialed, dated, and returned to the Evidence Unit (see Figure 8.3).

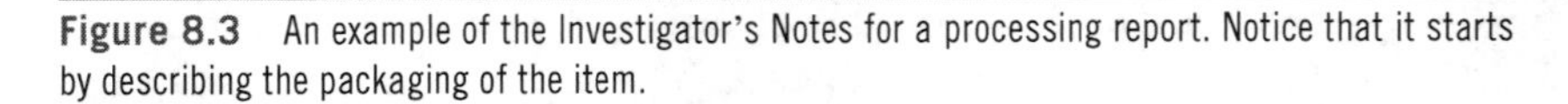

Investigator's Notes:

Item #770.1 (laptop) was found packaged in a brown paper bag, sealed with red evidence tape, and initialed. Prior to fingerprint processing, the item was photographed. The laptop had damage to all four corners and scrapes along the sides. The item was processed for latent fingerprints utilizing black magnetic powder. Latent print #01 was recovered.

All items were packaged, sealed, initialed, and submitted to the Evidence Unit at the [illegible] Office.

Figure 8.3 An example of the Investigator's Notes for a processing report. Notice that it starts by describing the packaging of the item.

Laboratory Processing

When a CSI collects evidence, or someone else collects evidence, the CSI may bring the items to the laboratory for processing. Depending on the agency, the available laboratory processing options will vary. Most agencies will have a variety of chemicals, powders, and laboratory equipment that may be utilized for different processing methods. The CSI may choose any method appropriate for the item they are processing. When the CSI processes these items, they will need to clearly explain in their report which item(s) they processed, what process(es) they used, and the results. Always report any results, even if they are negative. This will help the CSI to know why they moved onto other processes, if applicable. This also lets the reader know that processing was attempted. The laboratory processing information will go chronologically in the report and can be summarized in charts, if there are a multitude of items, or in straightforward sentences. The CSI will develop their own preference with experience (see Figure 8.4).

After the CSI finishes processing, the items will be repackaged, if they are previously submitted items, or newly packaged and submitted to the Evidence Unit. A chain of custody (COC) must be continued or started for all items submitted.

Chain of Custody

CSIs must remember to continue the chain of custody and properly document the items they are processing or begin a chain of custody for new items. A ***Chain of Custody (COC)*** is the chronological record of the handling and storage of an item from its point of collection to its final return or disposal that keeps track of every person who has handled the item of evidence, the dates and times the item was moved,

Items recovered from the vehicle were processed utilizing various methods. Below is a summary of the processing and the results:

Item	Description	Processing	Results*
619.1	One (1) scratch off lottery ticket	Magnetic powder/Ninhydrin	LOV
619.2	Two (2) scratch off lottery tickets	Magnetic powder	Negative
619.3	One (1) empty cardboard box	Magnetic powder	Negative

The lottery tickets in Items #619.1-.2 were numbered 1-3 for identification purposes. Ticket #1 was packaged separately (Item #619.1) due to positive results.

Figure 8.4 Charts may be utilized to summarize the processing of several items.

EVIDENCE/PROPERTY RECEIPT

Time of Seizure	1453	Incident Date	10/11/YR	Case #	
Date of Seizure	10/16/YR	ORI#	FL0180000		

☒ Evidence ☐ Found Property ☐ Destroy ☐ Safe Keeping ☐ Return To Owner

☐ Photographed & Returned: Sworn and subscribed this ___ day of ____, 20__ Signature: ________ Print Name:

ADDRESS WHERE PROPERTY WAS IMPOUNDED: LOCATION WHERE PROCESSING IS BEING DONE AND ITEMS RECOVERED

REPORT HEADING: Stolen Vehicle

	DOB:	Race/Sex	FULL ADDRESS	PHONE #
OWNER/VICTIM: IF KNOWN				
DEFENDANT/SUSPECT				
CO-DEFENDANT				
CO-DEFENDANT				

Item #	DESCRIPTION OF ITEM (Type, Make, Model, Color, Serial #, Marks, etc.)	Recovered Stolen
515.1	Racetrac bag, earbud, ear plugs, brown case	☐ Yes
515.2	Key Charm	☐ Yes
515.3	Change purse w/ misc receipts and paper tickets	☐ Yes
515.4	$0.67 in US currency, x1 dime, x57 pennies, and key charm earring	☐ Yes
515.5	LP #01-03	☐ Yes
515.6	DNA swabs #01-02	☐ Yes
	——————NOTHING FURTHER——————	☐ Yes
		☐ Yes

PROPERTY OWNER

I hereby acknowledge that the above list represents all property taken from my possession or returned to me and that I have received a copy of the report number. All items received for safekeeping or found must be claimed within 90 days or it will be disposed of in accordance with Florida Statutes 960.001(1) (h), 705.104 and 705.105.

Signature:

Print Name: ________

EMPLOYEE

I hereby swear/affirm that the above list represents all property ☒ impounded, ☐ returned or ☒ photographed by me in the official performance of duty as an employee of the FCSO.

Employee Signature: ________ ID #

Printed Name: CSI NAME

ITEM	DATE	RECEIVED FROM	DELIVERED TO	REASON
515.1-515.6	10/16	CSI NAME	Forensic Unit Temp Storage D	Evidence Processing
515.1-515.6	10/19	CSI NAME	Evidence Unit Locker	Evidence

Figure 8.5 An example of a chain of custody for new items recovered by the CSI.

and the location of the item at all times. When the CSI retrieves the items of evidence there should be an original COC with the items. The CSI should continue this COC, indicating when they retrieved the items and when they returned them. Any new items recovered should be entered onto a new COC (see Figure 8.5).

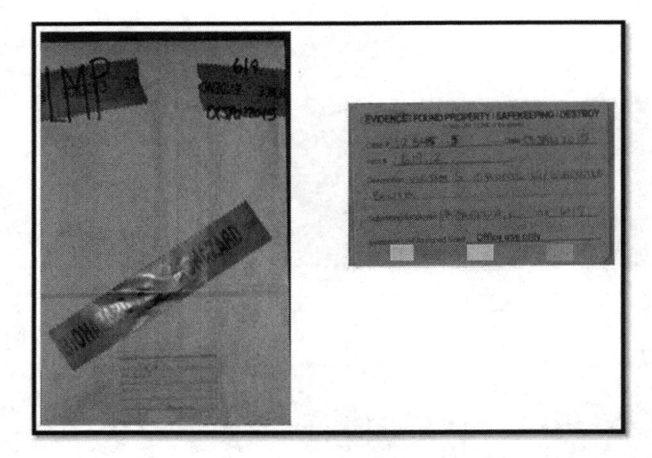

Figure 8.6 Packaging example. If CSIs were going to process this item, they would want to open any side not sealed with red evidence tape.

All items of evidence retrieved should be in packaging that is sealed and initialed. The CSI should not cut the taped seal; instead, they should open an opposite side of the package. After processing is complete, the item will be returned to the same package and the opening sealed and initialed by the CSI. This method of opening packages allows others to know how many times an item's packaging has been opened and will help with confirming the information on the COC (see Figure 8.6).

Summary

CSIs often get involved in the processing of evidence recovered by other members of their agency. In these cases, a thoroughly detailed report of the processing that was completed by the CSI will need to be completed. The CSI should write these reports chronologically beginning with how they were notified their assistance was needed. They should detail all processing they completed and the results. Maintaining a proper chain of custody is imperative in these cases.

End of Chapter Questions

1. What is a Processing Report?
2. What is a COC?
3. Why is it important to write in the report negative results?
4. Why are details such as serial numbers important?

9

General Guidelines for Writing Reports for Cases Involving Advanced Forensic Techniques

LAURA PAZARENA

Introduction

CSIs will implement a variety of advanced techniques over their career. Advanced techniques may include the application of a variety of chemicals for processing in the lab or on a crime scene, but the majority of CSIs get involved in advanced techniques surrounding the documentation of bloodstains and gunshot trajectory. A CSI is not required to be a bloodstain or ballistic expert, they are crime scene investigators, but they should have a thorough understanding of bloodstains and ballistics and how to properly document them for an expert to analyze. A part of being a crime scene investigator is the thorough documentation of all evidence and properly recording and documenting the scene in order to reconstruct the events that took place. Proper documentation of bloodstains and gunshots is critical to support testimonial evidence.

Bloodstains

CSIs often get called to crime scenes that involve a substantial amount of blood and bloodstain patterns. These scenes have ***bloodshed events***, which is the event or action that led to bloodstains on the scene. Often, the CSI can tell where the bloodshed event occurred by observing the different patterns on the scene. There are numerous pattern types that a CSI should be familiar with in order to have

DOI: 10.4324/9780429343162-12

proper conversations with investigators on the scene and with the experts. An important note is that a CSI is not a bloodstain expert unless they obtain the specialized training and experience involved to become one. Therefore, CSIs should not use blood spatter terms in their report, they should only state that "suspected blood" or "an apparent bloodstain" was observed". This eliminates the possibility that they will need to testify or explain terms beyond the scope of their knowledge or field testing. The CSI should always document in their field notes and report where they are observing the bloodstain patterns and they must use the correct terminology in regard to what they are seeing. As previously mentioned, the CSI will not refer to the pattern type, but only that what they are seeing is known as bloodstains. A ***bloodstain*** is a deposit of blood on a surface. A ***bloodstain pattern*** is a grouping of distribution of bloodstains that indicates through regular or repetitive form, order, or arrangement, the manner in which the pattern was deposited ((AAFS Standard Board #1-2) (see Figure 9.1)). The CSI is not observing ***splatter***, which is the action of a liquid falling onto a surface.

The CSI should document where they are observing the bloodstains and bloodstain patterns and based on what they are seeing they may often be able to determine where the bloodshed event began. When the CSI describes the "blood" it is always "suspected" or "possible". CSIs do not know definitively if the product they see on the scene, that appears to be blood, is in fact blood. CSIs should always report "blood" as suspected, possible, or any other similar term, even

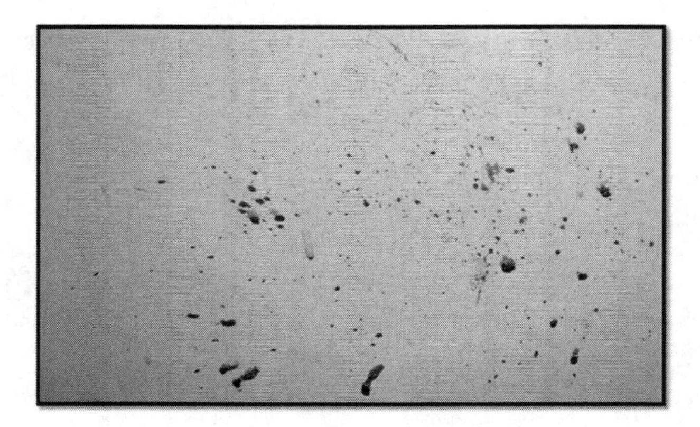

Figure 9.1 An example of a bloodstain pattern.

when field testing of the blood is undertaken because field tests often are presumptive, not conclusive, and have limitations of false negatives and false positives.

Similar to the scene description, bloodstains should be explained by general to a specific location. Bloodstains are often an "anomaly" on a scene, which means these are not always present and when they are present, they appear different every time. After a thorough description of the characteristics and conditions of the scene, the CSI should discuss anomalies such as bloodstains. The CSI should indicate exactly where they are seeing suspected blood by using directionals such as north, south, east, and west. The description should match the photos and clearly explain where the possible blood is located. For example:

> On the north wall of the living room, there appeared to be a 2-foot by 3-foot area of suspected bloodstains.

Once the observation of the bloodstains is complete, the CSI will need to apply advanced processing techniques. During the advanced techniques for bloodstains, the CSI will conduct testing to determine if the product is possibly blood.

CSIs should always photograph the scenes in situ before doing anything else. ***In situ*** means "as found". The CSI must document the scene exactly as they see it through photos and then begin their advanced techniques. After a scene with blood has been documented in situ the CSI may begin determining if there is in fact blood on the scene by conducting a presumptive test. ***Presumptive tests*** are screening tests that will tell the CSI the possible nature of the product being tested, although the test result does not constitute the identification of the material. There are presumptive tests for items such as drugs as well as blood. The CSI will want to presumptively test a variety of the stains before they begin their extensive documentation procedure. When testing, the CSI should select stains from different sections of the scene and should indicate how far apart these tested stains were. If the scene suggests the possible presence of multiple bleeders, CSIs should take this into account when deciding which and how many stains to test for the presumptive presence of blood. Depending on the amount of blood, and the length of any blood trails, the CSI may take samples from one or two stains closer together or may decide to take samples six inches to a foot apart. The spacing between the samples will be determined by the CSI and the scene. The presumptive test most frequently used for blood on crime scenes is known as the ***Kastle–Meyer Test***. This test uses a chemical known as ***phenolphthalein*** which reacts with the heme molecule in blood and will turn pink (see Figure 9.2).

When the CSI does the Kastle–Meyer test they need to indicate how many samples they took, how far apart they were, and the results for each one. Many times, this can be done in a chart or table. As discussed previously, using (and documenting) controls on the Kastle–Meyer reagent before testing scene samples would serve to verify the performance of the chemical. Something for CSIs to remember is that the swabs used in the presumptive test cannot be used for subsequent analysis. Thus, the CSI will need to collect fresh evidentiary samples for submission to a laboratory for further testing and analysis. The evidentiary samples will need to be listed in the CSI report as items of evidence.

Before collecting the evidentiary samples, the CSI needs to thoroughly document and label the bloodstains. The way documentation of bloodstains is done may vary greatly depending on the type of scene and bloodstain patterns. Bloodstain documentation is generally done through extensive photography. There are several ways the CSI can document bloodstains and based on the CSIs experience, preference, and the scene itself, the way they choose may vary. As mentioned, the CSI should be knowledgeable of different patterns on the scene and try to document those together. Although there are several documentation options for bloodstains, some of the most common are roadmapping, the grid method, and perimeter ruler.

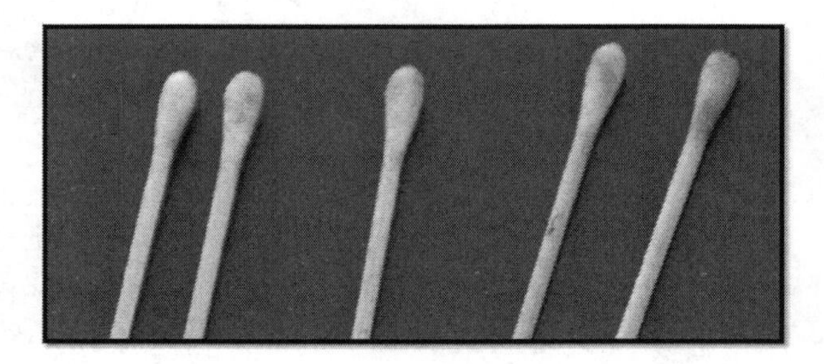

Figure 9.2 The bright pink color indicates a positive Kastle–Meyer test. These tested samples would be discarded, and sterile evidentiary samples would be collected.

Roadmapping

Roadmapping is a very common method of bloodstain documentation and CSIs should almost always implement this, especially if they are collecting samples of blood from the scene. This method can be combined with any of the other methods to further explain what the CSI saw on scene and tested. ***Roadmapping*** is when the CSI identifies various stains and labels them with scales and labels. The CSI will write the label of the stains on the adhesive scale and then adhere the scale next to the stain, being careful to not cover any portions of the stain. Several stains should be chosen, labeled, and photographed (see Figure 9.3).

After documenting the stains, the CSI should collect evidentiary samples from these labeled stains. When writing these items in the report, they should be listed under the "Swab" section and should clearly indicate that they are from that specifically labeled stain. For example:

Item #07: One (1) manila envelope containing Swab #01 labeled as follows:

> Swab #01: One (1) swab of suspected blood recovered from Stain #01.

Writing the evidentiary swabs in this way allows the reader to fully understand where the sample was collected from and what the sample is of. The explanation of where Stain #01 is located on the scene will be in the Investigator's Notes section of the report.

Roadmapping should be clearly explained chronologically in the report after the overall explanation of the spatter location. Not only does the CSI need to clearly write the swabs in the evidence portion of the report, but they must also explain how they identified and labeled the stains. The written description must match the photographs. When explaining the roadmapping, CSIs should use directionals and state which way they labeled the stains. Continuing with the general bloodstain example from above, roadmapping could be worded like this:

> On the north wall of the living room, there appeared to be a 2-foot by 3-foot area of suspected bloodstains. Several stains were labeled from west to east as "Stain #01" through "Stain #04". The labeled stains were approximately 1 ¼ inch apart. Stains #01-04 tested positive using the Kastle-Meyer test and evidentiary samples (Items #07-10) were recovered.

9.3a: Midrange photo of roadmapping on bloodstains on a floor.

9.3b: Close-up of Stain #01.

Figure 9.3 Example of roadmapping. Several stains are selected, and rulers are placed next to them. The stains are then labeled and sampled.

This succinct explanation describes the location of the overall spatter, the roadmapping that was done, the testing that was completed, and the samples collected in a couple of brief sentences. This is where the reader will now understand the exact location of Stain #01 and where Item #07 from the above evidentiary example was recovered. They now understand that the swab was recovered from the westernmost stain on the north wall of the living room. The photos will coincide with this labeling and further support the evidence explanations already provided.

Grid Method

The ***grid method of documentation*** is when the CSI creates a grid pattern over the bloodstain using string or chalk. Each grid is then numbered or lettered, and the grids and stains are then photographed (see Figure 9.4). CSIs should ensure they are including all ranges of photos (overall, midrange, and close-up) to show the viewer the exact location and labeling of the grid and stains.

Often, roadmapping is implemented with the grid method to show where specific stains are in the grid. Similar to the explanation of roadmapping, the CSI needs to explain how they implemented and

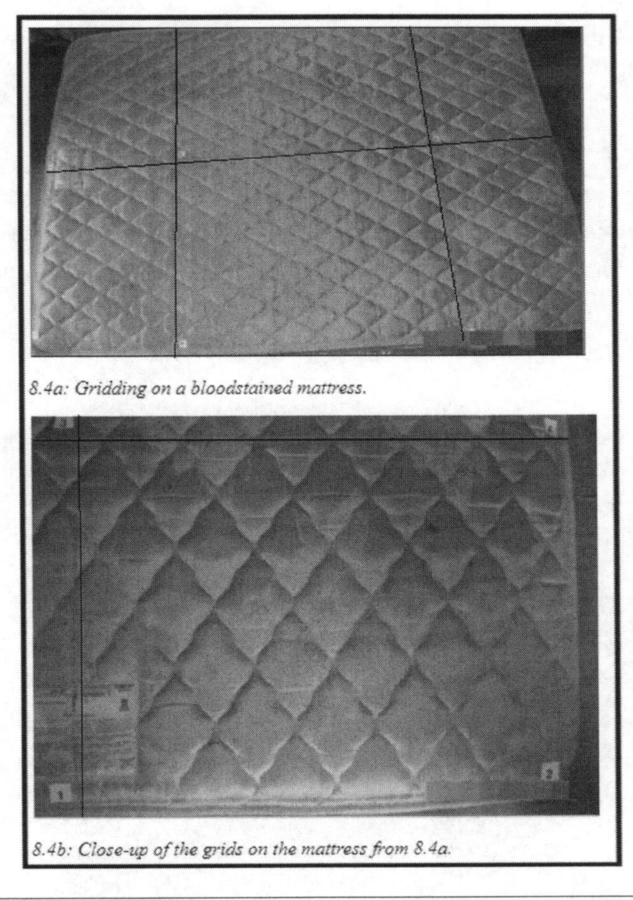

8.4a: Gridding on a bloodstained mattress.

8.4b: Close-up of the grids on the mattress from 8.4a.

Figure 9.4 An example of gridding. Each grid is numbered and then photographed with the numbers overlapping so that the viewer can see the stains in each grid.

labeled the grid in their report. Using the previous example, the CSI could write the grid method in their report in the following manner:

> On the north wall of the living room, there appeared to be a 2-foot by 3-foot area of bloodstains. This area was labeled using grids. Each grid was numbered 1-9, from west to east. Several stains were then labeled from west to east as "Stain #1" through "Stain #04". The labeled stains were approximately 1¼ inch apart. Stains #01-04 tested positive using the Kastle Meyer test and evidentiary samples (Items #07-10) were recovered.

In this example, the reader can now review and compare the photos and understand the exact location of each stain within the grid. This is very helpful to bloodstain experts when doing an analysis of the scene through the CSI's photos.

Perimeter Ruler

Perimeter ruler method of documentation is when the CSI places a ruler vertically and horizontally around the outermost edge of the bloodstain pattern. This allows the viewer to see the size of the pattern as a whole (see Figure 9.5). This also can be implemented in combination with roadmapping and the grid method. When photographing these patterns, the CSI must pay attention to their aperture settings and ensure the rulers are not blurry in the photos.

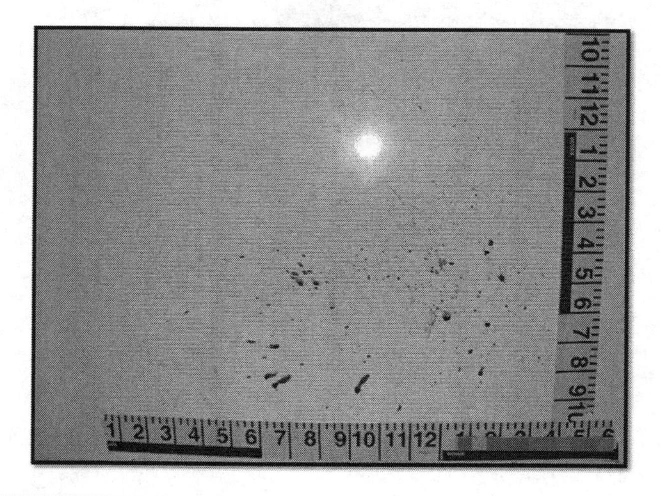

Figure 9.5 An example of a perimeter ruler.

Perimeter rulers do not need to be labeled or numbered and are mostly used for photographically documenting the size of the pattern; therefore specifically mentioning the perimeter ruler in the report is not always necessary. A CSI may mention them and would want to clearly indicate which side of the stain (north, south, east, or west) they placed each ruler. Adding perimeter ruler to our previous example could be written like this:

> On the north wall of the living room, there appeared to be a 2-foot by 3-foot area of bloodstains. A perimeter ruler was placed on the north and west sides of the stain. This area was then labeled using grids. Each grid was numbered 1–9, from west to east. Several stains were then labeled from west to east as "Stain #01" through "Stain #04". The labeled stains were approximately 1¼ inch apart. Stains #01-04 tested positive using the Kastle-Meyer test and evidentiary samples (Items #07-10) were recovered.

The documentation method chosen is up to the CSI. They may choose to implement one or a combination of them. In the report, the CSI wants to ensure they are clearly explaining the method they chose and that it matches their photos.

Chemical Processing of Blood

The previous documentation discussed visible blood, patterns of blood that the CSI can see when they walk into the scene. Oftentimes the CSI will arrive at a scene and the blood will be latent. ***Latent*** means that the blood is not visible until it is processed. Many times, this is what the public sees on television shows when a CSI is using a light source in a dark room and patterns are appearing. As discussed in earlier chapters, this is a challenge for a CSI. A CSI must be able to explain the scientific chemical processes they are using to enhance or develop blood on a scene and explain it to the court. There are several enhancement and development chemicals for blood. Some of the chemicals used for blood processing include, but are not limited to, amido black, luminol, and leucocrystal violet. Each one of these chemicals reacts with a specific portion of blood to enhance or develop the latent patterns. Chemical processing such as this should always be the last step of crime scene processing due to the possible destructive nature of the chemicals. CSIs want to ensure they are listing this processing in the report chronologically and detailing what chemical they used and the results. The CSI should understand how and why the chemicals work, but these specifics do not necessarily need to be in the report. Let's say the CSI chooses to process the north living room wall from our previous example using luminol. They could write that processing after they have explained their documentation like this:

> On the north wall of the living room, there appeared to be a 2-foot by 3-foot area of bloodstains. A perimeter ruler was placed on the north and west sides of the stain. This area was then labeled using grids. Each grid was numbered 1-9, from west to east. Several stains were then labeled from west to east as "Stain #01" through "Stain #04". The labeled stains were approximately 1¼ inch apart. Stains #01-04 tested positive using the Kastle-Meyer test and evidentiary samples (Items #07-10) were recovered. After samples were recovered, the remaining portion of the north wall was processed for suspected latent blood utilizing luminol with positive results. An additional area west of the visible stain of approximately 1 foot by 1 foot was made visible after luminol processing. This area was photographically documented.

The usage of chemicals does not have to be a complicated explanation in the report. The report should tell the reader what chemical was used, where, and the results including controls, if applicable. All of the scientific reactions taking place, or not taking place, should be able to be explained during testimony by the CSI. In this example, the luminol was "positive", which means there was a reaction between the chemical and heme on the wall. The CSI then needs to explain the approximate size and location of the newly visible suspected blood. This area will then be photographically documented. If the reaction when applying the luminol was "negative" the CSI would indicate this as well.

Shooting Scenes

In addition to blood, CSIs often get involved in cases involving gunshots. CSIs are not ballistic experts, and they are not making comparisons on the scene or determining what type of weapon may have created the defects they are observing. The CSI is responsible for the thorough documentation and labeling of any possible firearms-related evidence observed on the shooting scene including impact sites, cartridge casings, projectiles, firearms, and/or other ammunition components. Again, their documentation may be used by experts afterward to help reconstruct the events. CSIs should be familiar with firearm and ballistic terms to be able to discuss with investigators on the scene. CSIs want to ensure they are writing factually and make statements in their report such as "there was a possible entrance shot located …". The CSI does not want to make statements such as "there was an entrance shot located …". Referring back to previous chapters, this will ensure the CSI will not need to testify to topics outside of their knowledge.

Depending on the type of case and the needs of the investigation CSIs may be asked to conduct trajectory analysis on the scene or through vehicles back in the lab. Any firearm evidence that a CSI observes on the scene should be documented thoroughly through photos and labels. Similar to bloodstains, roadmapping is also used for projectile impacts and defects. Regardless of the number of visible impacts or defects or the ability to conduct trajectory analysis, CSIs should roadmap any visible impacts or defects on a crime scene. When roadmapping impacts and defects, the labeling should be done the same as bloodstains, using directions (north, south, east, or west), and the description should always start general and get more specific. After the general scene description is complete, the CSI will explain the specific location of the impacts and defects. For example:

> On the north wall of the living room there appeared to be three projectile impacts.

When roadmapping these three impacts the CSI wants to explain the direction they are labeling and the specific label they are using. Projectile impacts and defects may be labeled using small adhesive scales; if necessary, the CSI will write the label of the defect on the scale and then adhere it next to the defect on the wall, being careful to not cover any portion of the defect or any soot that may be present (see Figure 9.6). Each defect will then be photographed.

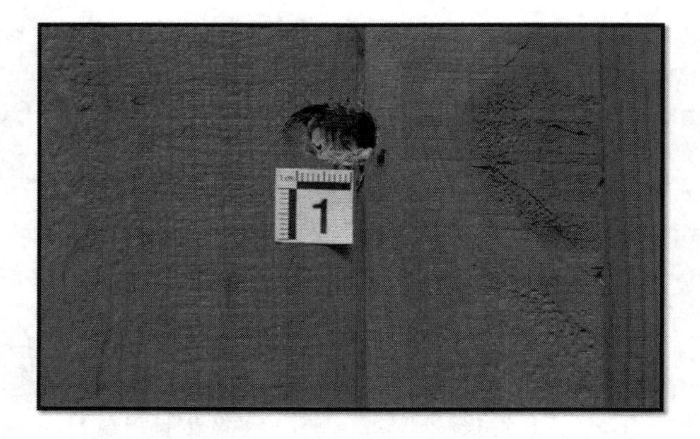

Figure 9.6 An example of roadmapping defects in a wall. In this instance, the scale was pre-printed as "1", if it had not been the CSI could write the numbering on the scale themselves.

Roadmapping of the previous example might be written like this:

> On the north wall of the living room there appeared to be three projectile impacts. The apparent defects were labeled as Defect A01 through Defect C01 from west to east.

This labeling will match the associated photographs. Just as with bloodstains, the CSI should photograph using all ranges to show the viewer the exact location of the defects in the wall. An important note about photographing similar defects, the CSI wants to go from close-up to midrange to close-up, not close-up to close-up. This means the CSI will want to photograph the entire wall showing all three defects, then do a midrange showing defect 1 and defect 2 in the same image, then a close-up of defect 1. After this close-up, they want to reorientate the viewer by taking a midrange of defects 1 and 2 in the same photo again and then the close-up of defect 2. This allows the viewer to follow the defects in the photos from west to east which also matches the written report.

Trajectory

Trajectory analysis is the use of calculated projectile impact angles that will help determine the flight path of a projectile. This becomes very important in cases where investigators are trying to determine the direction a shooter was aiming and their position. ***Impact angles***

are angles that the projectile strikes a surface. To determine trajectory the CSI must calculate the horizontal and vertical impact angles. The ***vertical impact angle*** is the angle measured to a virtual horizontal plane and will tell the up/down direction of the projectile – also known as the elevation angle. The ***horizontal impact angle*** is the angle measured to the vertical plane and will tell the right/left direction of the projectile – also known as the azimuth angle.

In order to conduct a reliably defined trajectory analysis, the shot must go through two items. This means the shot must go through the exterior and interior of a vehicle door or through a wall – also known as a ***perforating impact***. When a CSI has a scene in which there is a "through and through" shot like this, they may be asked to calculate the projectile's trajectory. The measurements for trajectory must be taken on the scene; therefore the CSI must ensure they get all measurements while there to allow them the ability to calculate trajectory at a later time. Since there are defects on two sides of the wall, the CSI must clearly indicate in the report where the shots are located. Let's say our three defects on the north living room wall from our previous example have aligned defects on the south kitchen wall. Based on a CSI's experience, they should be able to determine which side they *believe* to be the entrance and exit. Again, the CSI will not report the defects as "entrance" and "exit"; they will want to say "apparent", "appeared to be", or some other similar wording when writing these in the report. The CSI should be prepared to explain in court why they thought one was the entrance and the other the exit. If the CSI were to describe these gunshots, they could write something like this:

> On the north wall of the living room there appeared to be three entry projectile impacts. There were three suspected exit defects on the south kitchen wall.

After the entry and exit defects have been described, the CSI will roadmap the impacts on both walls. They must clearly explain how the defects on both sides of the wall are labeled, again using directions as a reference.

> On the north wall of the living room there appeared to be three entry projectile impacts. There were three suspected exit defects on the south kitchen wall. The defects on the north living room wall were labeled

as Defect A01 through Defect C01 from west to east and the shots on the south kitchen wall were labeled as Defect A02 through Defect C02 from west to east.

Many agencies have angle finders that CSIs may implement on a scene to help them find the impact angles of gunshots. If a CSI works at an agency without this equipment, they may still find the impact angles through measurements. This is a skill that CSIs should learn and be able to explain in court. In order to find the impact angles using measurements, the CSI will need to take specific measurements from certain fixed points. The measurements needed are:

- The floor to the center of each defect (these are used for the vertical impact angle; see Figure 9.7)
- The edge of the wall to the center of each defect (these are used for the horizontal impact angle; see Figure 9.8)
- The distance the projectile went through the wall (this is needed for both impact angles).

In order to find the distance the projectile went through the wall, the CSI will need trajectory rods. The CSI will gently insert the rod into the holes in the wall and then use a marker to mark where the projectile entered and exited the wall. The rod is then removed, and the distance measured. The distance the projectile went through the wall is not the width of the wall (unless the projectile struck the wall at 90 degrees). The projectile traveled at an angle which

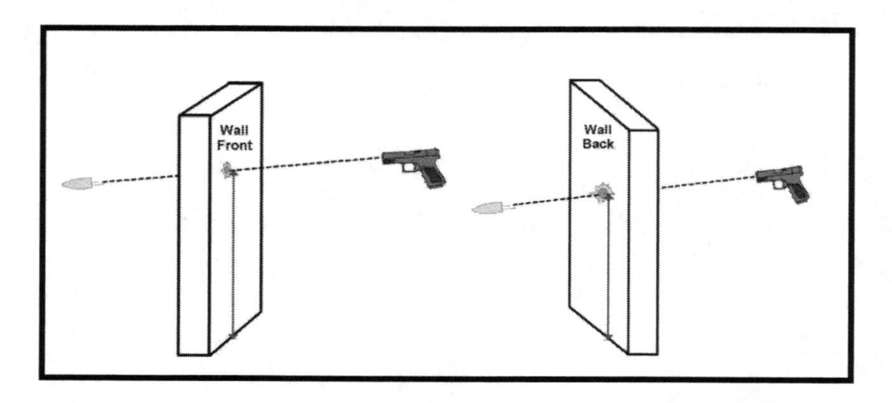

Figure 9.7 When calculating the vertical impact angle, the CSI needs to measure from the floor to the center of each defect on both sides of the wall.

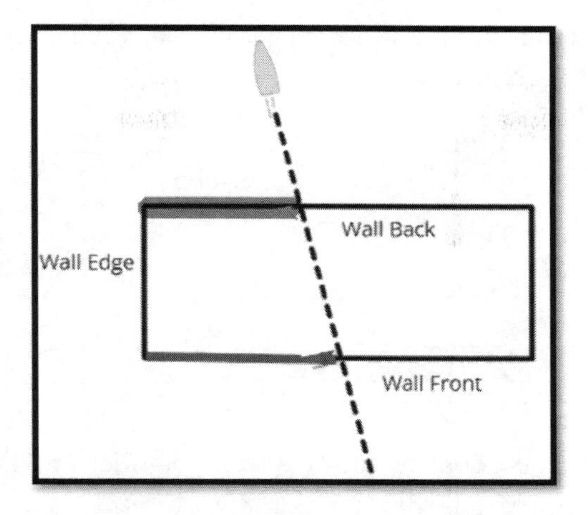

Figure 9.8 When calculating the horizontal impact angle, the CSI needs to measure from the edge of the wall to the center of each defect on both sides of the wall.

changes the distance traveled through the wall. It is important the CSI measures this correctly in order to calculate the trajectory. Measuring tapes can be used to measure the distance from the floor and the edge of the wall. In the CSI's notes, they will want to write all of these measurements and ensure they indicate which edge of the wall they are measuring from (north, south, east, or west). This is imperative for readers to be able to match the report to the sketch. Similar to taking notes of measurements for items on scene, creating a table or chart will help the CSI to keep all of these measurements organized.

All of these measurements will be put into trigonometry equations to calculate the impact angles. The calculations should be in the CSI's notes and should be understandable enough for them to refer back to them years later and recall how they calculated the impact angles. For the report, the CSI does not need to include all of the calculations but should include all measurements that correlate with the sketches. Summary charts are a good way to clearly explain measurements and impact angles in the report.

Let's add impact angles for the projectile impacts we have been discussing. First, we need to complete the field notes on the scene and obtain all measurements. The entrance defects were on the north living room wall and the exit defects were on the south kitchen wall. The CSI needs to take the measurements from the floor to each defect on both the living room and kitchen walls. In their notes they could create a chart such as this:

DEFECT	FLOOR TO DEFECTS ON LIVING ROOM WALL	FLOOR TO DEFECTS ON KITCHEN WALL
A01	23 inches	----------------------------------
B01	25 inches	----------------------------------
C01	15 inches	----------------------------------
A02	----------------------------------	24 inches
B02	----------------------------------	27 inches
C02	----------------------------------	18 inches

In addition to the floor measurement for each defect, the CSI needs the measurements from the edge of the wall to the defect on both the living room and kitchen walls. Again, a chart can be used to quickly write these measurements:

DEFECT	EAST EDGE OF LIVING ROOM WALL TO DEFECTS ON LIVING ROOM WALL	EAST EDGE OF KITCHEN WALL TO DEFECTS ON KITCHEN WALL
A01	8 inches	----------------------------------
B01	10 inches	----------------------------------
C01	13 inches	----------------------------------
A02	----------------------------------	9 inches
B02	----------------------------------	11 inches
C02	----------------------------------	15 inches

The CSI will then use rods to measure the distance each projectile went through the wall. In this case we will say Defect A = 2.5 inches, Defect B = 3 inches, and Defect C = 4 inches. The CSI now has all the measurements needed to complete the calculations for impact angles. The CSI will complete the math in their notes, draw the sketches, and need to explain the results in the report. The CSI should remember that the formatting of how this portion of the report is written is individual to the CSI, their preferences, and their agency policy and procedures. Here is an example of how the report summary of these defects with the trajectory could be written:

> On the north wall of the living room there appeared to be three entry projectile impacts. There were three suspected exit defects on the south kitchen wall. The three defects on the north living room wall were

labeled as Defect A01 through Defect C01 from west to east and the defects on the south kitchen wall were labeled as Defect A02 through Defect C02 from west to east.

The horizontal and vertical impact angles were calculated using measurements for the projectile impacts on the scene. Below is a summary of measurements and angles for all defects (also see associated diagrams):

DEFECT	FLOOR TO DEFECTS ON LIVING ROOM WALL	FLOOR TO DEFECTS ON KITCHEN WALL	EAST EDGE OF LIVING ROOM WALL TO DEFECTS ON LIVING ROOM WALL	EAST EDGE OF KITCHEN WALL TO DEFECTS ON KITCHEN WALL	DISTANCE THROUGH WALL	VERTICAL IMPACT ANGLE	HORIZONTAL IMPACT ANGLE
A01	23 inches	-----------	8 inches	-----------	2.5	24° Up	-----------
B01	25 inches	-----------	10 inches	-----------	3	42° Up	-----------
C01	15 inches	-----------	13 inches	-----------	4	49° Up	-----------
A02	-----------	24 inches	-----------	9 inches	2.5	-----------	66° Left
B02	-----------	27 inches	-----------	11 inches	3	-----------	70° Left
C02	-----------	18 inches	-----------	15 inches	4	-----------	60° Left

The above is showing only the projectile impacts and the measurements. Always remember to write chronologically. Oftentimes the trajectory math and calculations will not be completed until much later in the investigations, but the measurements will be taken on the scene. If this occurs the paragraph discussing the trajectory and measurements can be separated and placed in chronological order in the report.

Summary

CSIs will be involved in a variety of cases and investigations throughout their career. Many of these cases will involve advanced forensic techniques to document bloodstains and projectile trajectories. The CSI should familiarize themselves with the applicable terminology for advanced techniques and use them appropriately in the report. Bloodstains and projectile trajectories should be thoroughly documented through photographs and in writing. The explanations must be clear to the reader and be written chronologically to fully explain what the CSI did to process when this was done, and what the results were.

End of Chapter Questions

1. What is a bloodshed event?
2. What is the difference between a bloodstain and a bloodstain pattern?
3. What is roadmapping, and why is it important to a CSI?
4. What are three documentation methods that may be utilized for bloodstains or defects believed to be from gunshots?
5. What is a perforating impact?
6. What measurements must a CSI obtain on the scene in order to do trajectory analysis?

Reference

AAFS Standard Board. *Terms and Definitions in Bloodstain Pattern Analysis.* ASB, 2017. https://asb.aafs.org/wp-content/uploads/2017/11/033_TR_e1_2017.pdf.

SECTION 4
TESTIFYING IN COURT

10

Testimony Related to CSI Reports

AMY WATROBA

Preparing for the Pre-trial Meeting

A CSI called upon to testify about a scene and/or evidence that they processed should always have at least one meeting with the attorneys who will present them as a witness in advance of the trial or proceeding. During this ***"prep" or "pre-trial" meeting***, the CSI's report and expected testimony should be discussed.

The best thing a CSI can do to make the pre-trial meeting as fruitful as possible for both the CSI and the involved attorneys (usually criminal prosecutors) is to review their reports and materials before the pre-trial meeting. This way, the CSI will not spend precious minutes or hours of the pre-trial meeting reviewing reports and refreshing their recollection about the case but instead will be able to focus on going through their anticipated testimony, asking questions of the prosecutors, and answering any questions the attorneys may have about the case. In short, a CSI should walk into the pre-trial meeting ready to hit the ground running.

Before the pre-trial meeting, the CSI should review all of their notes, diagrams, photographs, and reports and, where applicable, watch any videos taken of the crime scene. With respect to physical evidence collected from the scene, the CSI should use their materials to remember where the recovered items were with respect to the crime scene as a whole. It might be helpful to the CSI to mentally work through and review the scene in the same manner that they did when they processed it, using their documentation to remind themselves of when, why, and how they did what they did.

DOI: 10.4324/9780429343162-14

In most cases, the "prep" meeting will be a meeting with criminal prosecutors. Due to the busy nature of most prosecutors' schedules, this meeting likely will take place close in time to the trial itself. The pre-trial meeting may also be limited in time because prosecutors frequently meet with all witnesses in the weeks and days before trial. While the onus of scheduling the pre-trial meeting generally is on the prosecutor, a CSI who is scheduled to testify and has not heard from the prosecutor in the weeks leading up to the scheduled trial should reach out to the prosecutor to ask about the status of the case and to let the prosecutor know that the CSI would like to have a "prep" prior to testifying.

The Pre-trial Meeting

Ideally, the prosecutors will have familiarized themselves with the CSI's report(s) before the pre-trial meeting and will have a general outline of how they plan to conduct the CSI's direct examination. In reality, this is not always possible due to the prosecutors' schedules and caseloads. If the prosecutor is not prepared to take the lead during the pre-trial meeting, the CSI should feel free to walk the prosecutor through the scene and case, using their reports, notes, and other materials.

During any pre-trial meeting, the CSI also should feel free to ask for clarification about anything that the prosecutor says about the case or the trial proceedings that is unclear to them. Some questions a CSI might have during a pre-trial meeting might be:

> Are there any pre-trial rulings related to my testimony that I should be aware of or parts of my report or items of evidence that the court has ruled I am not allowed to talk about during trial?
>
> What kinds of questions should I expect on cross examination?
>
> If I am cross examined about _____, do you plan to ask me any re-direct questions about that topic?
>
> What physical exhibits are you going to show me or ask me to identify?
>
> What photographs do you plan to use during my testimony?
>
> Are you going to play any videos during my testimony? If so, do you plan to ask questions of me contemporaneously with the playing of the video or after it is played?

During any communication with the prosecutor, the CSI absolutely should clarify or correct any misunderstandings or incorrect conclusions that the prosecutor may have drawn from reviewing reports, notes, photographs, or videos. Remember, the prosecutor was not present at the scene, so even if the CSI's documentation is clear to them, a prosecutor may still misread, misunderstand, or misinterpret something.

Finally, and most importantly, if a CSI notices any mistakes in their report, notes, or any of their other materials at any time, the CSI should bring the mistake(s) to the prosecutor's attention immediately. Based on the nature of the mistake and the rules of the jurisdiction, the prosecutor will then decide what action(s) will need to be taken to correct the mistake prior to trial and to notify the opposing party and the court. This could include requesting the issuance of an amended report in some circumstances. If it is determined that an amended report will need to be issued, the CSI should not stress about it. Everyone is human and makes mistakes. It is much better to catch an inaccuracy or mistake in a report prior to trial than to discover it for the first time when the CSI is on the witness stand at trial.

Testifying

It should go without saying that a CSI should always testify truthfully whether they are testifying formally under oath or in some other type of setting. A CSI also should dress and act professionally when testifying about a case. Some agencies may have protocols that address matters such as uniform and decorum during testimony. The CSI should familiarize themselves with any applicable rules or protocols and adhere to them.

A CSI likely will testify most frequently in court during bench or jury trials. The CSI should know their audience in the case, so to speak. If the case is being decided by the judge (***bench trial***), the CSI should direct their answers toward the judge. If the case is being decided by the jury (***jury trial***), the CSI should direct their answers toward the jury.

The CSI should listen carefully to the questions asked by the attorneys and answer only what is asked. If the CSI does not understand the question, they should so state. If a question is asked and a lawyer raises a legal objection (usually by audibly saying "objection"), the CSI should not answer the question, but rather wait until the judge instructs the CSI as to whether they may answer the question. Again, the CSI must always answer truthfully and if that requires the CSI to provide an expanded answer or indicate that they cannot answer the question posed with a simple response, they should do so.

The CSI should maintain a calm and professional demeanor at all times, even if the attorney questioning them becomes upset, accusatory, frustrated, or angry. This can be difficult, especially during a lengthy or intense cross-examination about a complicated case. Ideally, testimony should be conversational between the witness and the person asking the questions, even during cross-examination. Mastering the art of testifying takes time and practice, so the CSI should take advantage of any opportunity they are afforded to observe others testifying in court and/or to participate in mock trial exercises.

Use of CSI Report during Testimony

As discussed in more detail in Chapter 11, written materials such as the CSI's report and notes generally will not be admitted into evidence at a trial. The reports may, however, be used during the CSI's testimony to refresh the CSI's recollection about the case or to point out perceived inconsistencies within the documents or between the documents and the CSI's testimony. The manner in which the documents are used usually will depend on whether the documents are being referred to during direct examination or cross-examination.

Direct examination is the questioning of a witness by the party that called the witness for the purpose of presenting evidence in support of their case. Most frequently, a CSI will be called as a witness as part of the Government's case and, therefore, a prosecutor will conduct the direct examination.

During direct examination, the questioning attorney will ask open-ended questions and the witness will provide the details during their answers. The questioning attorney is permitted to present the question in context but is not allowed to suggest what the witness's answer should be by asking what is known as a "leading question".

If the attorney asks a CSI a question during direct examination and the CSI cannot recall the answer without referring to their report or notes, the attorney may utilize the CSI's documents to refresh their recollection. Procedures for doing this differ by jurisdiction, but the questioning frequently will resemble the following example:

Prosecutor: Did you inventory the knife under inventory number 123456?
CSI: I don't recall the specific inventory number.
Prosecutor: Is there anything that would refresh your recollection as to what inventory number you inventoried the knife under?
CSI: Yes.
Prosecutor: What is that?
CSI: My CSI report.
Prosecutor: (approaches the CSI and hands them their report) I'm showing you what I have marked as Government's Exhibit 10 for identification purposes. Do you recognize this?
CSI: Yes.
Prosecutor: What is it?
CSI: It is my CSI report from this case.
Prosecutor: Please take a look at your report and let me know when your recollection is refreshed as to the inventory number of the knife.
CSI: (after reviewing the report silently) My memory is refreshed.
Prosecutor: (takes the report away from the CSI before asking the question) Did you inventory the knife under inventory number 123456?
CSI: Yes.

Cross-examination is the questioning of a witness by the adverse party, or the party that did not call the CSI as a witness. During cross-examination, the attorney is allowed to ask leading questions that suggest an answer. These questions frequently may be answered with a simple "yes" or "no" response. However, the questions may suggest a fact, inference, or conclusion that is either incorrect or that the CSI does not have knowledge about. As such, the CSI should listen very carefully to the question asked and determine (1) whether the CSI can answer the question, and (2) if a truthful answer requires more than just a "yes" or "no" response.

The CSI's report or notes may be used during cross-examination if the CSI does not remember a fact from their report or to point out a perceived inconsistency or flaw in the report or testimony. Either way, the report will be used in a manner that is more confrontational than the refreshing recollection procedure discussed above, even if the CSI just does not remember something. This is generally referred to as using documents for impeachment purposes. It is important that the CSI not get upset or agitated if they are "impeached" on the stand. And, if an inconsistency or mistake exists, the CSI must testify truthfully about it.

Again, procedures for using a document for impeachment differ by jurisdiction, but the questioning may resemble the following example:

Defense Attorney: You testified earlier that you inventoried the gun under inventory number 123457?

CSI: Yes.

Defense Attorney: You wrote a report in this case, correct?

CSI: Yes.

Defense Attorney: You wrote this report close in time to when you inventoried the evidence?

CSI: Yes.

Defense Attorney: And it is important to be accurate in your reports, correct?

CSI: Yes.

Defense Attorney: And in your report, you wrote that you inventoried the gun under inventory number 123458?

CSI: I don't recall.

Defense Attorney: (handing the report to the CSI) I'm showing you what is marked as Defense Exhibit 1 for identification purposes. This is your CSI report, correct?

CSI: Yes.

Defense Attorney: And directing your attention to the portion of the report where you list the items you inventoried, you indicate that you inventoried the gun under inventory number 123458, correct?

CSI: Yes.

Defense Attorney: Inventory 123457 is actually a sock, correct?

CSI: Yes.

Defense Attorney: So, your earlier testimony about the inventory number for the gun was incorrect?

CSI: Yes. I made a mistake about the inventory number for the gun in my testimony.

As previously discussed, a CSI should remain calm and professional at all times on the stand. This is especially important in situations where the CSI is challenged or "impeached" with something from their report or their notes during cross-examination. If an attorney points out a legitimate mistake, inconsistency, or omission, the CSI must testify truthfully and acknowledge it. While a CSI may understandably feel uncomfortable when they are confronted with a mistake or omission at trial, as the CSI becomes more experienced and practiced at testifying in court, they will realize that acknowledging a mistake in a non-defensive manner will actually *add* to the credibility of the CSI's overall testimony about their work on the case, rather than detract from it.

Summary

Testifying in court takes preparation, especially when the trial could be months or years after the CSI worked on the case. The best thing a CSI can do to prepare to testify in court is to develop good report writing skills in the first instance, as outlined in previous chapters. A CSI should review their report, notes, sketches, as well as any photographs and videos in advance of the pre-trial meeting with attorneys to prepare for their trial testimony. The pre-trial meeting is an excellent opportunity for the CSI to ensure that they are able to clearly and accurately explain the work they did on a case to someone (usually the prosecutor) who was not present at the scene. When the CSI is on the witness stand during the trial, it is imperative that they listen carefully to the questions asked, that they testify truthfully, and that they maintain a professional demeanor at all times.

End of Chapter Questions

1. What is a pre-trial meeting?
2. What should a CSI do if they notice a mistake in their report before trial?
3. What is direct examination?

4. What is cross-examination and how does it differ from direct examination?
5. What should a CSI do if an attorney raises an objection to a question when they are on the witness stand?
6. Why is it important to acknowledge mistakes while testifying?

11

Legal Challenges to CSI Reports and Testimony

AMY WATROBA

Discovery Issues

In both criminal prosecutions and civil proceedings, the parties to the litigation will receive and/or have access to CSI reports and other documents, photographs, video recordings, audio recordings, and physical items related to the CSI reports. The timing and nature of the access that the legal parties have to the CSI reports and related materials will vary by jurisdiction and are generally governed by a particular jurisdiction's statutes, court rules, discovery rules, evidentiary rules, and case law. The mechanism by which CSI reports will be tendered to the parties also may vary by jurisdiction and even by case. For example, CSI reports may be requested via a subpoena issued by one or both parties, by court order, and/or by regular practice and procedures established between law enforcement agencies and prosecuting authorities.

The tendering of materials to and between legal parties is referred to as ***discovery***. It is important that the CSI and the CSI's agency tender all discovery materials in accordance with agency guidelines and applicable laws. Failure to tender or disclose materials could result in the exclusion of evidence from trial or the reversal of a conviction during a direct appeal or post-conviction proceeding. If at any time the CSI learns that discovery materials were inadvertently omitted or not disclosed, they should immediately bring this information to the attention of their supervisor and the prosecuting agency.

Objections to Aspects of a CSI's Reports or Testimony

Even if the CSI is just testifying about the scene, what they saw and documented, and what they did to collect and preserve evidence, the

DOI: 10.4324/9780429343162-15

opposing party may raise challenges to certain aspects of the CSI's testimony.

As discussed in previous chapters, the CSI's report generally will not be admitted into evidence at a trial because it is ***hearsay***. The rule against hearsay may be relaxed in some jurisdictions during pre-trial or post-trial hearings, so it is possible that the report could be admitted into evidence in those contexts.

Diagrams or drawings included as part of the CSI's report may also be objected to as hearsay, but parties may nonetheless be permitted to use them at trial as ***demonstrative evidence***, which is evidence that is used to assist the witness in testifying and explaining their testimony to the jury without being admitted for consideration as evidence in and of itself.

Photographs and videos taken by the CSI at the crime scene are not statements made by the CSI, so they are not objectionable on hearsay grounds. However, in order to have those admitted into evidence and used at trial, the CSI will have to lay the required foundation for their admission. ***Foundation*** refers to the facts necessary under a jurisdiction's rules to admit evidence which establishes that the evidence is what it purports to be and that it is relevant to the case. Foundation is usually established by the attorney asking a series of "who, what, when, where, and how" questions. For example, to admit a photograph the prosecutor may ask the CSI what time the photograph was taken, who took the photograph, who else was present when the photograph was taken, where the photograph was taken, and what the photograph shows. The prosecutor also may ask a question to establish that the photograph truly and accurately depicts the crime scene as it appeared to the CSI when they were on scene. If an attorney fails to establish the requisite foundation for an exhibit, the opposing party may successfully argue that the exhibit should not be admitted, which would mean that the CSI cannot testify about it.

Other types of technical evidence, such as videos or materials recovered from a computer, or a cell phone will have additional foundational requirements that must be established before the CSI will be permitted to testify about them. The prosecutor should go over these foundational questions with the CSI during the pre-trial meeting. If a video of the crime scene was taken and it contains audio, the court may rule that the video be redacted to exclude the audio because the audio aspect of the recording contains hearsay statements of those present on the scene.

Objections related to a CSI's expected testimony may occur before trial when the parties file **motions *in limine***, which seek rulings in advance of trial on evidentiary issues. Usually, motions *in limine* are based on legal arguments made by the parties, but occasionally testimony from a CSI may be required if there is a factual issue that impacts the legal arguments. Motions *in limine* generally deal with issues that will require more argument from the parties, such that saving them for trial will require taking extended breaks from the presentation of evidence, or that might impact a party's trial strategy such that they want a legal ruling on the admissibility of certain evidence so that they can plan their case theory accordingly.

For example, if a CSI performed field testing on the scene to try to locate possible biological stains (e.g., Blue Star or an alternative light source), and the defense wants to completely bar the CSI from testifying about that action, that challenge would likely be raised in a motion *in limine*.

In contrast, objections claiming that the CSI has failed to lay the appropriate foundation for admission of a video because the prosecution did not ask all of the required questions would likely be raised contemporaneously while the CSI is on the witness stand. As previously discussed, if an objection is raised during a CSI's testimony, they should wait to obtain a ruling from the judge before answering the question. If the objection is ***overruled***, that means that the judge has determined that the question was proper and may be answered by the CSI. If, on the other hand, the objection is ***sustained***, that means that the judge has determined that the question was improper and that the CSI cannot answer the question as asked. If an objection is sustained, the CSI should not answer the question. Depending on the reason for the judge's ruling, the attorney may rephrase the question or move on to another topic. If the attorney rephrases the question and the opposing party does not again object, then the CSI may then answer the new question.

Physical Evidence

The admission of physical exhibits (items recovered or processed by the CSI) will require an adequate foundation and possible additional questions to establish the chain of custody. Questions about the chain of custody are asked to ensure that the item collected at a scene is the same item that was later processed at another location or laboratory and that it is the same physical item being presented in court. Questions related to the chain of custody are very technical in nature and refer to things like item numbers, inventory numbers, seals on the packaging, the CSI's markings on the packaging, etc. If a CSI lists and describes the evidence in an organized and accurate manner as outlined in previous chapters, then establishing the chain of custody for physical items at trial should not be difficult and there should be little room for objections to the admission of physical evidence on this basis.

Forensic Samples

If the CSI processes an item on the scene or in another location for latent print impressions, collects swabs or samples for DNA testing, or conducts any type of field testing for the possible presence of blood, for example, the CSI must be able to explain their methodology. Where applicable, the CSI should be able to testify to the basics of the underlying science (e.g. discussion of what an alternative light source is and what types of substances illuminate when an ALS is used).

The CSI also should be prepared to testify about the training they received in how to perform the method or test at issue, as well as what they actually did in that particular case. A CSI's inability to adequately explain their training, the general methodology used, or what they did in the case could result in an objection to the admission of that evidence on foundation or relevance grounds.

Examples

1. The CSI should be able to describe how they swabbed a suspect blood stain by removing the sterile swabs from sealed packaging, how they used the swab to collect a sample from the suspect bloodstain, how they packaged and sealed the swabs, and how they labeled and inventoried the swab.
2. If the CSI collected a buccal swab from an individual for a DNA reference sample, the CSI should be able to describe the buccal swab collection kit, how they used the swabs in the kit to swab in the inside of the individual's mouth, and how they sealed and packaged those standards.

3. If the CSI processes an item for latent print impressions, the CSI should be able to explain what they used to try to develop the latent impression (e.g. dusting powder, cyanoacrylate fuming), and how that technique helps develop latent print impressions. The CSI also should be prepared to testify about what they observed after attempting to develop a print, how they conducted the lift of the impression, and/or how they took a digital image of the impression.

Expert Witness Rules

In very general terms, an ***expert witness*** is a witness who is permitted to testify in court to opinions based on their specialized knowledge, skill, experience, training, or education related to a particular subject matter or discipline. Every jurisdiction has its own rules and case law regarding who may testify as an expert witness and what an expert witness may testify about. Thus, if a CSI testifies as an expert witness at a hearing or trial, additional rules will govern the admissibility of their testimony and may provide additional bases for challenging some, or all, of their testimony. The attorneys presenting the CSI as a witness should be familiar with the rules and case law in their jurisdictions and account for them in their plans for the CSI's direct examination. Generally, testifying as an expert witness will require the CSI to answer more questions about their professional background, training, and the methodologies used in the case. This is because generally there will be additional foundation requirements for the CSI to testify to any "expert" conclusions or opinions about case evidence (e.g., offering opinions about crime scene reconstruction or bullet trajectory).

If the CSI is testifying as an expert witness, any major challenges to the admissibility of their opinions most likely will take place before trial. A hearing may be held prior to trial to address the general subject matter or discipline of the proffered testimony, the CSI's particular qualifications to testify regarding the subject matter, the methodologies employed in that particular case, or the scope of the proffered testimony. The CSI may be called as a witness at a pretrial hearing related to admissibility issues. Their testimony at this hearing may address both their work in the particular case and the broader scientific principles or specialized knowledge underlying their "expert" opinions or conclusions.

If the CSI who processed the scene also conducted testing or analysis that calls for them to render expert opinions, the CSI may testify in a dual role – as both a lay witness and an expert witness. A ***lay witness*** is a person who does not have expertise about the subject matter of their testimony such that they are qualified to give expert opinions in court. Most witnesses who testify during trials are lay witnesses – including eyewitnesses to the crime, police officers, and CSIs. If a CSI testifies in a dual role as a lay witness and an expert witness, the CSI's testimony will need to satisfy the foundation requirements for both types of testimony. It is possible that objections will be raised to a CSI testifying in their capacity as an expert, but not to their testimony about the processing of the scene. It is important that the CSI speak to the attorney who will present them as a witness prior to trial to ensure that the CSI does not inadvertently discuss the evidence in a manner that would run afoul of any rulings by the judge about the permissible scope of the CSI's testimony at trial.

Summary

Legal rules and principles may limit how and what a CSI may testify about in court. Attorneys often will obtain legal rulings from the judge prior to trial about the admissibility of evidence that the CSI documented in their report, collected, or tested. It is imperative that a CSI is aware of and understands the basic rationale behind any pretrial rulings related to their testimony before they testify so that the CSI testifies consistently with court rulings. Additionally, contemporaneous objections may be made while a CSI is on the witness stand that impacts what the CSI is permitted to testify about in "real time". If a CSI has a general understanding of legal concepts such as objections and foundation requirements for the admission of evidence, the CSI will be better prepared to move forward and testify effectively even if their testimony is unexpectedly impacted by legal rulings rendered during the trial.

End of Chapter Questions

1. What is discovery?
2. What is demonstrative evidence?
3. Why is a CSI sketch or diagram considered demonstrative evidence in court?
4. How can a CSI easily testify to the chain of custody using their report?
5. What are some differences in the way a CSI would testify as a lay witness versus an expert witness?

12
Conclusion

MICHAEL KESSLER

Despite the nature of the scene a CSI is tasked with processing – from burglary to homicide – one of the primary tasks is the documentation of the scene and the items contained within it. Documentation is an essential component of scene investigation. The quality and completeness of the documentation are critical to ensure a complete recording of the scene. While this documentation can take many forms – notes, sketches, digital images, 3D laser scans, and reports – it serves to provide a detailed record of the scene for all future investigative and judicial purposes.

Recording the condition, position, and location of physical evidence prior to collection provides critical information and context to the investigation. A well-documented scene ensures the integrity of the investigation and provides a permanent record for later evaluation. Failure to accurately and completely document the crime scene may negatively impact subsequent forensic analysis, including crime scene reconstruction, and the admissibility of evidence during judicial proceedings. In general, the position and condition of decedents and other significant forensics material should be recorded prior to removal, collection, or alteration.

The documentation of a scene as part of the investigation is a continuous process in which the observations, aspects, actions, and procedures of the scene and evidence are contemporaneously and comprehensively recorded from start to finish. Thorough and accurate documentation of the scene and all items recovered from it has a three-fold basis of significance: investigative, scientific, and legal. Scene documentation creates a fair, factual, and accurate record of the actions, observations, and conditions at a given scene and its immediate surroundings using various documentation methods and

DOI: 10.4324/9780429343162-16

technologies. It provides the basis from which a detailed report and scene reconstruction could be created using the documentation alone and it also memorializes all work performed such that another examiner could evaluate what was done and understand the basis of the observations and results.

Notes

Notes should be taken continuously throughout the scene investigation and thoroughly document all investigative efforts. Included in the documentation should be observations of the scene as it appears, and items deemed of potential evidentiary value. In addition to contextual data about the scene (date, location, time), transient evidence (odors, sounds) and conditions (weather, temperature) should also be noted. Just as any processing done on the scene should be documented, so should any situations which require deviation from standard procedures.

Sketches

A sketch visually presents the circumstances and positions in which evidentiary items were located within a scene. Sketches of the scene, together with other relevant documentation, should enable all items of potential evidentiary value to be located at the scene and the relation of such evidence items to other objects and evidence items. Sketching is used to specifically describe the location of items of potential evidentiary value in situ prior to collection, the location of items of potential evidentiary value relative to other objects present and other potential evidentiary items, and the physical scene. Final sketches accurately convey the size, shape, and position of significant items and other features of a scene. A rough sketch or multiple rough sketches may be used to note the location where objects and evidence items within the scene serve to supplement written notes, and document measurements for use in creating the final sketch.

The Scene Report

The scene report is the documentary culmination of the entirety of the effort by the CSI. The majority of the consumers of the report will never observe the CSI in action or visit the scene, yet they must fully be able to understand what the CSI did and the appearance of the scene down to fine details. Through the CSI's report, the reader should understand all of the work done at the scene as well as the decisions and considerations that went into the scene examination.

A well-written scene report should be succinct – containing all of the required detail while presented in an as short and simple format as practical. It should also be accurate – reporting facts based on the physical evidence, results of processing, and first-hand observations. The report should be objective – making no conclusions and presenting no theories. Lastly, it should be complete – presenting the facts as they are known, scene considerations as they were found, physical forensic evidence as it was recovered, and processing activity as it occurred.

Information regarding evidence processing, handling, and collection decisions made by the CSI should also be included. Completely documenting these aspects prevents the potential inference that potential processing methods or evidence items were overlooked or not considered properly. Both positive and negative processing results must be thoroughly recorded to ensure an accurate and thorough record of the scene examination. As the old saying goes, if it's not in the report it didn't happen. Failing to fully document all observations and processing actions subjects the CSI to scrutiny about the handling of and adequacy of their on-scene examination.

CSI reports should be uniform and consistent in presentation, format, and style. The consumers of scene reports – detectives, lab scientists, reconstructionists, and attorneys – will all have expectations about what the report should contain and how the material should be presented given their experience in reading similar reports. This consistency is expected and required for efficiency and the prevention of errors and miscommunication.

The scene report will be the CSI's main tool to inform their courtroom testimony. As investigations often go to trial several years following the conclusion of the scene investigation, the CSI's notes and scene report are the only source of information a CSI may rely upon to refresh their recollection about the case in court. With the passage of time and the examination of multiple scenes, details will fade and the lines between scenes will blur.

Short bibliography

AAFS Standard Board. *Terms and Definitions in Bloodstain Pattern Analysis*. ASB, 2017. https://asb.aafs.org/wp-content/uploads/2017/11/033_TR_e1_2017.pdf.

Gardner, Ross M. *Practical Crime Scene Processing and Investigation*. Third ed., Boca Raton, FL, CRC Press, 2019.

https://www.merriam-webster.com/dictionary/succinct.

Appendix 1

Crime Scene Section Investigative Report

CASE NUMBER:	CSI:	DATE (of the incident):	DATE (of processing):	APPROX. TIME (of processing):
COMPLAINANT, VICTIM, WITNESS, DECEDENT, SUSPECT:		INCIDENT::		APPROX. TIME (on the scene)
LOCATION OF INCIDENT:				APPROX. TIME (depart scene)

Case Overview:

On DATE at approximately TIME hours NAME received a call HOW from WHO requesting WHAT in reference to WHAT TYPE OF CASE. MEET WITH WHO, THEY SAID WHAT. The following services were provided:

Weather:

TEMP, AND GENERAL CONDITIONS

Vehicle:

ANYTHING RELEVANT TO THE SCENE

Diagram:

A diagram of WHAT was completed by WHO (SCALE OR NOT) and CAN BE FOUND WHERE.

Digital Images:

HOW MANY digital images were taken of WHAT by WHO with a digital camera and CAN BE FOUND WHERE.

Video:

HOW MANY videos were taken of WHAT by WHO and CAN BE FOUND WHERE

Items of Evidence:

Item #__ (***Photo Placard #__***): QUANTITY, WHAT IS IT, COLOR, LABELINGS, RECOVERED FROM WHERE.

Prints:

Item #: HOW MANY, HOW LABELED, RECOVERED FROM WHERE

Swabs:

Item #: HOW MANY, HOW LABELED, RECOVERED FROM WHERE

Investigator's Notes:

DESCRIBE THE SCENE

DESCRIBE ANY ANOMALIES ON SCENE – MAY OR MAY NOT BE NEEDED

DESCRIBE DECEDENT/VICTIM – MAY OR MAY NOT BE NEEDED – INCLUDE TRANSPORT OF THE BODY

DESCRIBE ADDITIONAL PROCESSING – ON SCENE OR IN THE LAB

STATE WHERE EVERYTHING WENT – GENERALLY THE EVIDENCE (AND/OR PROPERTY) UNIT.

Name of Employee Completing this Report		Date		ID #	
Supervisor Approval					

Appendix 2

Crime Scene Section Processing Report

CASE NUMBER:	CSI:	DATE (of the incident):	DATE (of processing):	APPROX. TIME (of processing):
COMPLAINANT, VICTIM, WITNESS, DECEDENT, SUSPECT:		INCIDENT::		
LOCATION OF INCIDENT:				

Case Overview:

On DATE at approximately TIME hours NAME received a call HOW from WHO requesting WHAT in reference to WHAT TYPE OF CASE. MEET WITH WHO, THEY SAID WHAT. The following services were provided:

Weather:

TEMP, AND GENERAL CONDITIONS (MAY NOT BE NEEDED)

Vehicle:

ANYTHING RELEVANT TO THE SCENE

Diagram:

A diagram of WHAT was completed by WHO (SCALE OR NOT) and CAN BE FOUND WHERE. (GENERALLY NOT NEEDED)

Digital Images:

HOW MANY digital images were taken of WHAT by WHO with a digital camera and CAN BE FOUND WHERE.

Video:

HOW MANY videos were taken of WHAT by WHO and CAN BE FOUND WHERE

Items of Evidence:

Item #__: QUANTITY, WHAT IS IT, COLOR, LABELINGS, RECOVERED FROM WHERE.

Prints:

Item #: HOW MANY, HOW LABELED, RECOVERED FROM WHERE

Swabs:

Item #: HOW MANY, HOW LABELED, RECOVERED FROM WHERE

Investigator's Notes:

DESCRIBE THE EVIDENCE AND THE PACKAGING

DESCRIBE ANY ANOMALIES WITH THE EVIDENCE – MAY OR MAY NOT BE NEEDED

DESCRIBE ADDITIONAL PROCESSING – IN THE LAB

STATE WHERE EVERYTHING WENT – GENERALLY THE EVIDENCE (AND/OR PROPERTY) UNIT.

Name of Employee Completing this Report		**Date**		**ID #**	
Supervisor Approval					

Glossary of Common Terms and Acronyms

ALS: Alternate light source; light sources that give off different wavelengths and assist in identifying a variety of forms of evidence.

Amido black: A chemical used to enhance visible blood. This chemical reacts with the proteins in the blood causing a dark blue/black color reaction.

Anomalies: Oddities about a crime scene often observed by a CSI during the walkthrough or their investigation.

Area of origin: The 3D location in a room of a blood source.

Baseline coordinates: A crime scene mapping method using a datum point and a baseline as fixed points.

Bench trial: The case is being decided by the judge.

Bloodshed event: The event or action that led to bloodstains on the scene.

Bloodstain pattern: A grouping of distribution of bloodstains that indicates through regular or repetitive form, order, or arrangement the manner in which the pattern was deposited.

Bloodstain: A deposit of blood on a surface.

BPA: Bloodstain pattern analysis; the evaluation of bloodstain patterns to help determine the events that took place at a bloodshed event.

Bullet: A commonly misused term; it is best to avoid the use of this term since the reader will often misinterpret what the physical item is, a cartridge versus the actual projectile itself. Most forensic experts use this term to refer to a projectile.

Cartridge: The unfired ammunition that is loaded into a firearm; composed of primer, cartridge casing, powder, and projectile.

Cartridge casing: The exterior portion of a cartridge that holds the other components; when a firearm is fired, this may have identifying features from the weapon.

Characteristics of the scene: Include the layout, floor plan, and general description of the location.

COC: Chain of custody; the chronological record of the handling and storage of an item from its point of collection to its final return or disposal.

Conditions of the scene: Refers to the cleanliness, level of disarray, forced entry, or any other descriptors that describe or help illustrate what the scene looked like.

Contamination: The introduction of foreign material to an object or scene.

Control: Material of known composition that is analyzed to evaluate the performance of a test to demonstrate that the method or equipment works correctly, and the results are valid.

Cross examination: The questioning of a witness by the adverse party or the party that did not call the CSI as a witness.

CSI: Crime scene investigator; a person responsible for the investigations of crime scenes and the documentation, preservation, and submission of physical evidence.

CSI report: A report written by a CSI to record – from start to finish – the procedures, observations, actions, and aspects of the scene and evidence within it.

Cutting: A cutout area of a piece of larger evidence that is submitted as evidence.

Cyanoacrylate ester: A viscous clear liquid used for the development of latent fingerprints on non-porous surfaces.

Decedent: An individual who has died.

Demonstrative evidence: Evidence that is used to assist the witness in testifying and explaining their testimony to the jury without being admitted for consideration as evidence in and of itself.

Direct examination: The questioning of a witness by the party that called the witness for the purpose of presenting evidence in support of their case.

Discovery: Tendering of materials to and between legal parties.

Expert witness: A witness who is permitted to testify in court to opinions based on their specialized knowledge, skill, experience, training, or education related to a particular subject matter or discipline.

Field notes: Notes, generally written by hand, while on a crime scene or processing in the lab.

Foundation: The facts necessary under a jurisdiction's rules to admit evidence which establishes that the evidence is what it purports to be and that it is relevant to the case.

Grid method of documentation: An option of documenting stains and defects in which the CSI creates a grid pattern using string or chalk.

GSR: Gunshot residue; the residue left on objects, individuals, or in the air after a weapon has been fired, often consists of antimony, barium, and lead.

Hearsay: Information that a CSI is told from someone else that they did not personally observe.

Horizontal impact angle: Also known as the azimuth angle; the angle in trajectory analysis that measured to the vertical plane and will tell the right/left direction of the projectile.

Hungarian red: A chemical used to enhance visible blood, fluoresces under green light (520–560 nm), and viewed with red goggles.

Impact angles: Angles that a projectile strikes a surface.

Initial briefing: A discussion done on the scene between a CSI and an individual familiar with the case.

Jury trial: The case is being decided by the jury.

Kastle–Meyer test: A presumptive test used by CSIs to test for blood on scenes.

Latent: Invisible until processed.

Lay witness: A witness who does not have expertise about the subject matter of their testimony such that they are qualified to give expert opinions in court.

LEO: Law enforcement officer; a person who has taken a sworn oath to enforce the laws of their jurisdiction.

Leucocrystal violet: A chemical used to enhance visible blood and develop latent blood. This chemical reacts with the heme group in the blood causing a violet color reaction.

LOV: Latents of value; an acronym that may be used to indicate that an item was processed for latent fingerprints, ridge detail was observed, and the ridges were identifiable.

Lt.: An abbreviation for the rank of Lieutenant.

Luminol/bluestar: A chemical used for the development of latent blood that reacts with the iron in blood to give off chemiluminescence.

Motions in limine: When attorneys seek rulings in advance of trial on evidentiary issues.

NLOV: No latents of value; an acronym that may be used to indicate that an item was processed for latent fingerprints, ridge detail was observed, but there were no identifiable portions of the ridges.

Overruled: One of the options a judge has in court in response to objections by the attorneys. This means that the judge has determined that the question was proper and should be answered.

Penetrating impact: A defect that goes through only one side of an object.

Perforating impact: A defect that goes completely through something; often called a "through and through".

Perimeter ruler method of documentation: An option of documenting stains and defects in which the CSI places a ruler vertically and horizontally around the outermost edge of the bloodstain pattern or defects.

Personal protective equipment (PPE): Tools used to protect the CSI from contaminants.

Pharmacist folds: Small envelopes that the CSI can create on the scene from any piece of paper.

Phenolphthalein: The chemical in the Kastle–Meyer test that reacts with the heme in blood to create a bright pink reaction.

Photo log: A list of every single photo that was taken, the settings on the camera, and what the photo depicts.

Photo placards: The numbers set out on a scene next to a physical item of evidence that is going to be collected by a CSI.

Point of convergence: The 2D location of a blood source.

Police report: A report written by a police officer about an incident or case, often includes testimonial evidence.

Presumptive tests: Screening tests that will tell the CSI the possible nature of the product being tested; although the test result does not constitute the identification of the material.

Pre-trial meeting: Meeting between the attorneys and their witnesses in advance of the trial or proceeding.

Projectile: An object that is expelled from a firearm when fired.

Prone: On the stomach.

Rectangular coordinates: A crime scene mapping method that uses two fixed points and measures at right angles to the center mass of the evidence.

Rhodamine 6G: A chemical used for the development of latent fingerprints that causes a fluorescent reaction after excitation with a blue/green light.

Roadmapping: The labeling of defects or stains with scales and labels.

Rough sketches: Hand-drawn sketches done on the scene in the field notes.

Sgt: An abbreviation for the rank of sergeant.

Shotgun cartridge: The unfired ammunition that is loaded into a shotgun; composed of primer, shotgun casing, powder, projectile(s), wad, and shotshell cup.

Stringing: The use of impact angles at a bloodshed event to determine the area of origin.

Supine: On the back.

Sustained: One of the options a judge has in court in response to objections by the attorneys. This means that the judge has determined that the question was improper and should not be answered.

Testimonial evidence: Statements people make that may be used as evidence.

Trajectory analysis: The use of calculated impact angles to determine the flight path of a projectile.

Triangulation: A crime scene mapping method utilizing regular and irregular shaped objects; two or four measurements are taken to set datum points.

Vertical impact angle: Also known as an elevation angle; the angle in trajectory analysis that is measured to a virtual horizontal plane and will tell the up/down direction of the projectile.

Victim: An individual who has suffered from events that have taken place.

Walkthrough: When an individual familiar with the case walks the CSI through the scene and the events.

Zone search: A method of searching in which the CSI divides the area to be searched into adjacent zones. Used for confined spaces like vehicles, or for vast areas that need to be broken down, such as acreage of land.

Index

PGIL2021USA